ENCYCLOPEDIA OF MAMMALS

VOLUME 5
Dog–Gal

MARSHALL CAVENDISH

NEW YORK • LONDON • TORONTO • SYDNEY

AFRICAN WILD DOGS

RELATIONS

African wild dogs belong to the mammal order Carnivora and the dog family, Canidae. Other members of the family include:

WOLVES

COYOTE

JACKALS

FOXES

DHOLE

RACCOON DOG

BUSH DOG

Matthews Purdy/Survival Anglia

The African wild dog is a member of the dog family, Canidae, which includes all the dogs, wolves, jackals, and foxes. The Canidae is one of seven families in the order Carnivora, a group of mainly predatory species distinguished by their meat-slicing carnassial teeth.

ORDER

Carnivora
(carnivores)

FAMILY

Canidae
(dogs)

GENUS

Lycaon

SPECIES

pictus

STRIPPED FOR ACTION

LEAN AND LIGHTWEIGHT, THE AFRICAN WILD DOG HAS SPECIALIZED AS A COOPERATIVE KILLER—A RELENTLESS HUNTER THAT PURSUES ITS PREY TO THE POINT OF EXHAUSTION BEFORE TEARING IT APART

Loping with leggy ease over the dusty baked earth of the East African plains, seven scrawny, color-blotched wild dogs reach a rise in the ground and gaze out on a predator's dream: vast herds of antelope, zebra, and gazelle scattered across an immense grassy plain extending to the horizon; a panorama of meat on the hoof. Slowing to a walk, the pack heads for the nearest group of wildebeest, or gnu, bunching together in a tight wedge with their dark muzzles and white-flagged tails held low, like a cloud shadow slipping over the close-cropped grass. The wildebeest see them and a ripple of panic spreads through the herd. The adults edge closer together to conceal the vulnerable calves, but too late. The dogs start to run, the wildebeest bolt, and the chase is on.

No other predator can run quite like the African wild dog. Even the cheetah, for all its feline grace and slingshot speed, cannot sustain a long chase like this ragged hunter. A wild dog is quite prepared to pursue

Gleaming ivory rows of deadly dental weaponry contrast starkly with the dark muzzle (below).

Franz J. Kamenzind/Planet Earth Pictures

its prey for three miles (5 kilometers) or more, running at a steady 30–37 mph (48–60 km/h). Running is its strategy and its strength: It rarely bothers to use stealth or ambush tactics. It simply runs, relentlessly, until its quarry can run no more, then drags it to the ground and tears it apart. This approach may not be subtle, but it works.

As athletes, the ancestors of the African wild dog were not in the same class. The early canids were omnivorous foragers with short legs and long, fairly weak jaws—consumers of small game and scraps, much like modern foxes. But some six million years ago changes in the climate led to an expansion of the grassy plains and scrublands at the expense of the forests, and these habitats were exploited by a new type of herbivore: swift hoofed animals equipped to outrun their enemies in the open instead of eluding them by slinking into cover. Yet although these animals were fast, they were—and are—relatively poorly protected, making them vulnerable to any predator that could catch them. It did not take long for the

African wild dogs greet each other excitedly, reinforcing the tight-knit bonds of the pack.

602

Steve Robinson/NHPA

PAINTED WOLVES

The wild dog is the most flamboyantly patterned of all the canids, with blotches of black, tan, yellow, and white splashed at random all over its body and legs. Its species name, *pictus*, actually means "painted." Since each individual dog sports a unique pattern, zoologists believe that the patterning may have a social function, enabling the dogs to recognize each other at a glance in the turmoil of the hunt; it may also act as a visual bonding device.

Alternatively the blotches may simply provide camouflage. All the evidence suggests that the African wild dog evolved as a hunter of scrubland and open forest, and in such habitats its patterning helps break up its predatory outline and allows it to get closer to its prey before being seen. It is of little value on open grassland, but then the prey itself has fewer opportunities to make a bolt for cover.

canids to develop a bigger, faster strain capable of exploiting this niche: the lineage that led to the wolves and hunting dogs of today.

These lupine (wolflike) dogs are typically long-legged, lightly built animals with heavier jaws than their vulpine (foxlike) relatives, but the African wild dog takes this tendency to extremes. Lean and sinewy, it carries roughly half the weight of a wolf of similar shoulder height. Its long legs are developed for running, with the lower leg bones strengthened and locked together to prevent twisting, three of the "wrist" bones fused together, and four sturdy, blunt, fixed claws on each foot for traction on hard ground. Its deep chest contains capacious lungs to increase oxygen absorption, giving it the stamina to outdistance virtually any other animal on the savanna.

BUTCHERY MADE EASY

This stripped-down racing frame carries a massive head that is fashioned to meet a very different set of priorities. With a relatively short, broad muzzle to increase the biting force of the jaw muscles, it is equipped for one purpose: the efficient butchering of fresh meat. The African wild dog has lost the ability to pulp the vegetable foods that supplement the diet of most other canids. Its cheek teeth—the meat-slicing carnassials characteristic of all mammals in the order Carnivora—have been refined into simple scissor-action blades that shear through skin, muscle, and sinew. By comparison the carnassials of other canids such as the wolf are dual purpose: They have slicing blades, but these also have small grinding surfaces backed up by a set of crushing molars at the back of the jaw. The dentition of the wild dog makes no such compromises, and the molars have become redundant. Meat is easy to digest, so it does not need to be chewed like tough plant material. The wild dog simply has to slice it into chunks and bolt it down before it is stolen from under its nose.

Yet although the teeth and jaws of the wild dog are massive by canid standards, they are filigree work compared with the heavy engineering of a big cat. A solitary lion can use the relentless power of its jaws to throttle the life from a full-grown zebra. Perhaps more important it has the weight and muscle—and the sharp, raking claws—to leap from ambush and fell the animal in its tracks. Such tactics are beyond the capacity of the lean and lightweight wild dog. A single dog may use a catlike throat bite to kill small prey, but anything larger than a slender gazelle can generally shake it off. So it has two options: It can hunt alone for small game, or it can hunt in packs.

Pack hunting is the speciality of the African wild dog. Other lupine canids have adopted the same strategy, but only three species—the African wild dog, the Asian dhole, and the South American bush dog—rely

---

THE AFRICAN WILD DOG IS EXCLUSIVELY CARNIVOROUS AND SIMPLY LACKS THE TEETH TO COPE WITH VEGETABLE FOODS

---

on it to the virtual exclusion of all other hunting methods. Where large prey is abundant, such cooperation has definite advantages, since acting together to kill a big animal generally provides more food for each individual than hunting solo. So up to the point where it becomes unacceptably dangerous, bigger is better, even if it takes teamwork.

There is more to teamwork than the reinforcement of muscle power, though. It also involves good communication, and the quick wit to act on it. Dogs are well equipped in both respects, for they are sociable by nature and social interaction is the most powerful factor in the development of communication skills and intelligence. Yet the teamwork goes deeper than this. The hunting pack is not a scratch team recruited for the day, but an extended family that lives as a single unit. They know everything about each other, and this gives them the ability to work almost telepathically in the excitement and confusion of the chase. It is this that makes African wild dogs so formidable, and yet so utterly reliant on each other that they are barely capable of surviving on their own. So each dog is simply the proverbial "small cog in the big machinery." ■

AFRICAN WILD DOG

Lycaon pictus
(lie-KAY-on PICK-tuss)

The most sociable of all the dogs, and the most highly developed pack hunter, the African wild dog probably evolved into a distinct type some four million years ago. Uniquely among dogs, it has only four toes on each forelimb, and this fact, coupled with its unusual social system and coloration, makes it one of the least typical of the canids. Sadly, it also has the least favorable reputation and has been mercilessly persecuted by humans. Now extremely rare and endangered, it survives in scattered packs on the savannas of eastern and southern Africa.

WOLF
JACKALS
COYOTE

SOUTH AMERICAN
FOXES AND
MANED WOLF

THE AFRICAN WILD DOG'S FAMILY TREE

The canid family tree is still debated by zoologists, but new techniques such as DNA analysis may eventually settle any disputes. One argument concerns the relationship between the African wild dog, the Asian dhole, and the South American bush dog. These three species were formerly grouped in a subfamily of their own because they have similar carnassial teeth and they are all pack hunters. The classification was discarded, but recent studies suggest that the three species are in fact distant relatives descended from an early offshoot of the lupine line—so perhaps the subfamily idea was valid after all.

BUSH DOG

B/W illustrations Ruth Grewcock

DHOLE

LUPINES

VULPINES (TRUE FOXES)

REDUNDANT THUMBS

In many animals, including ourselves, the first digit on the forelimb—the thumb—is extremely important. A strong thumb has all kinds of uses, and the dexterity it provides has probably been a major factor in the shaping of human culture.

But for a running animal like a dog, a thumb is of little practical use, so in most canid species it has been reduced to a small "dewclaw" that does not even touch the ground. Since the dewclaw stays relatively sharp, it may have some value as a weapon when subduing small prey, but it would make little impression on an animal the size of an antelope. Perhaps this is why, uniquely among dogs, the African wild dog has lost the "thumb" altogether.

Color illustration Steve Kingston

DOG FAMILY (CANIDAE)

ANATOMY:
THE AFRICAN WILD DOG

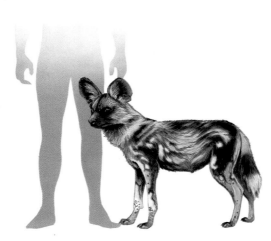

The African wild dog (above) is roughly the size of a wolf, but far more slender. Males and females are very similar in size, although males tend to be some 10 percent heavier than their sisters. For comparison, the Asian dhole has a similar build, while the bush dog of South America is barely the size of a badger (neither is shown above).

THE EARS

are mobile and unusually large, enabling the dog to use them for visual communication at long range. Well supplied with blood vessels, they act as heat radiators to help keep the dog cool in the tropical climate.

THE MUZZLE

is short and broad, and always black. The dog hunts mainly by sight and is less inclined to use scent signals than most canids, but despite this, its sense of smell is acute thanks to the large surface area of nasal membranes within its muzzle.

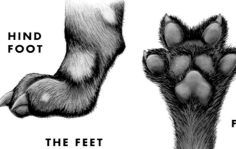

HIND FOOT

FOREFOOT

THE FEET
The African wild dog runs on its toes, with strong, nonretractile claws to increase grip at speed. Uniquely among canids, the wild dog has lost the dewclaw from each forefoot.

X RAY

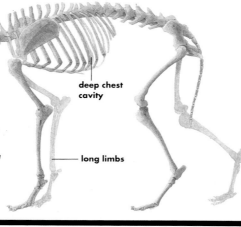

SKELETON
The African wild dog has a strong but relatively inflexible spine and a deep chest cavity to contain large-capacity lungs. Its limbs are specialized for running at speed, being elongated by extra long shoulder blades and a digitigrade stance. The collarbone, or clavicle, is redundant and has virtually disappeared.

deep chest cavity

long limbs

TEETH
The lower carnassial teeth have two knifelike cusps in line. These act against the upper carnassials like scissor blades to shear through tough hide, sinew, and flesh. In most other dogs, each lower carnassial has twinned rear cusps that form a flattened grinding surface for chewing tough vegetable food.

short, broad jaw

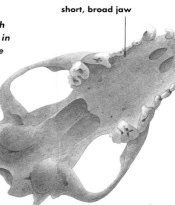

X-ray illustrations Elisabeth Smith

COAT PATTERN EXAMPLES

THE COAT

The fur is short and scant, and in older dogs it thins out even further to reveal the black skin beneath. The coat pattern is unique to each individual, but there are similarities between members of the same family.

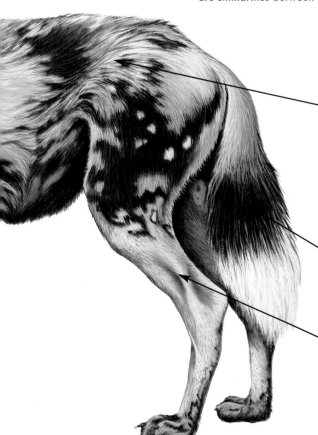

THE BODY

is lean but wiry, like that of any endurance runner. A deep chest contains the big lungs needed to obtain the oxygen to fuel long chases. Its elastic stomach enables it to gulp down up to 11 lb (5 kg) of meat at a sitting.

THE TAIL

is tasseled, and always has a conspicuous white tip; it is used as a visual signal to other dogs in the pack.

THE LEGS

are long and slender, but well muscled to propel the dog at speeds of up to 40 mph (65 km/h) as it closes on its prey.

FACT FILE:
AFRICAN WILD DOG

CLASSIFICATION

GENUS: *LYCAON*
SPECIES: *PICTUS*

SIZE

HEAD–BODY LENGTH: 30–40 IN (75–100 CM)
TAIL LENGTH: 12–16 IN (30–40 CM)
AVERAGE WEIGHT: 44–60 LB (20–27 KG)
MALES ARE SOME 10 PERCENT HEAVIER THAN FEMALES

COLORATION

SPARSE COAT OF RANDOM BUT WELL-DEFINED BLACK, TAN, YELLOW, AND WHITE BLOTCHES ON GRAYISH BLACK SKIN; IN OLDER ANIMALS THE SKIN IS CLEARLY VISIBLE. EACH INDIVIDUAL HAS A DIFFERENT COAT PATTERN, BUT THE MUZZLE IS ALWAYS BLACK AND THE TUFTED TAIL ALWAYS HAS A WHITE TIP

FEATURES

LITHE, SLENDER BUILD
LONG SLIM LEGS WITH FOUR TOES ON EACH FOOT
WHITE-TIPPED TAIL
BROAD, DARK MUZZLE WITH CONSPICUOUS TEETH
LARGE, ROUNDED EARS

SKULL

The jaw is broader and shorter than that of a more typical canid, such as a wolf. This increases the leverage that can be exerted on the long canine teeth by the big jaw muscles attached to the crest at the back of the skull, enabling the dog to hang on to powerful, struggling prey. The eyes face forward, giving the binocular vision essential for judging distances.

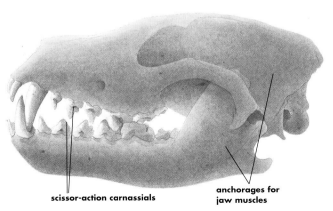

scissor-action carnassials

anchorages for jaw muscles

JAW MUSCLES

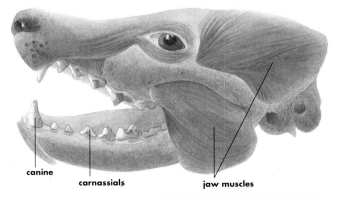

canine

carnassials

jaw muscles

Main illustration Kim Thompson

BLOOD BROTHERS

ROAMING OVER VAST TRACTS OF GRASSLAND AND SCRUB IN SEARCH
OF PREY, A WILD DOG PACK REPRESENTS AN ORGANIZED BAND OF
BRIGANDS BONDED BY TIES OF BROTHERHOOD AND MUTUAL NEED

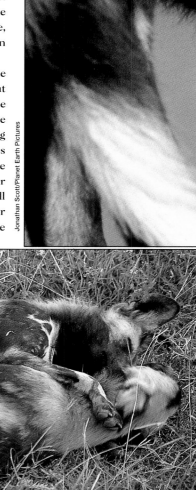

During the dry season the glaring midday sun over the African savanna could curl you to a crisp. Over vast expanses of parched grass there is no shade. The only respite from the heat lies in the dwindling, muddy water holes and the shallow gullies scoured out of the plain by the seasonal rains. Here the dry, powdery soil is laid bare, and scratching away the hot surface exposes a layer of earth that still retains a memory of the chill tropical night. In such secret places, barely visible from more than a few yards away, lie the wild dogs.

With their lean, blotched bodies pressed tight to the cool earth, or curled into ragged patchwork bundles in the dry grass, they lie stunned by the heat. Occasionally one rouses itself to dig a little deeper, but it soon flops down again to sprawl upon its little patch of cool earth. The odd flick of a white-tipped tail above the lip of the gully is the only sign that they are there. When the temperature drops toward nightfall, they will stir themselves to hunt; they may return to the gully for the night or they may rest elsewhere, for one camp is as good as another. They have no homes to go to: They are footloose ruffians, the gypsies of the plains.

NOMADS

For three months of the year a breeding wild dog pack is tied to a den—a cool burrow where the matriarch of the pack bears and rears her litter of pups—but for the remaining nine months they wander at will over the landscape, hunting at dawn and dusk, resting by night and day. In areas where the grazing remains viable throughout the year, they may not have to wander far, but on the sunbaked plains of the southern Serengeti in Tanzania, the dry season is heralded by a mass exodus of the grazing herds as they migrate in search of fresh pasture, and any dogs that prey on them must either follow

or travel far and wide to survive on the slim pickings that remain. Either way, they are in for several months of footsore trekking as they crisscross vast ranges of over 1,000 square miles (2,500 square kilometers) in the quest for food. While on the move, wild dogs rarely sleep in the same place more than twice in succession.

Each pack is dominated by the breeding pair—the so-called alpha female and her chosen mate—but most of the other adults are males. Some may be mature sons of the breeding pair, but others are likely to be the alpha male's brothers. For wild dog society, unusually, is held together by close bonds between males. Sisters typically squabble and strike out on their own, but brothers often hunt together and even help raise each other's young. They will welcome a group of roaming females into their midst, but generally only one remains to breed. The

Wild dogs kiss and cuddle to demonstrate the force of their loyalty toward each other (above).

INSIGHT

INNOCENT KILLERS

The African wild dog is widely regarded as a cruel, bloodthirsty killer, but this judgment is based on a human concept of morality that applies only to humans. Predators may occasionally kill more animals than they can eat, but this is usually because the prey cannot escape and repeatedly triggers the hunter's instinct to secure food while it can. There is no evidence that the killer takes any pleasure in inflicting pain. It kills to survive, just as a thrush kills a snail or a spider kills a fly. As written by George Schaller, zoologist for the Wildlife Conservation Society: "Nature has neither cruelty nor compassion. The ethics of man are irrelevant to the world of other animals. Dogs kill out of necessity, in innocence not in anger, hardly a situation to engender revulsion on the part of man."

dominant male normally sires all the pups, but his brothers respect blood ties and stay fiercely loyal.

As for violence, the wild dog is notorious. It has a reputation for savagery which is hard to refute, for although it simply kills to eat, it does so in a way that often looks unnecessarily cruel. The fact is that although wild dogs are good at catching their prey, they are poorly equipped to kill it. So rather than waste time and energy, they normally skip the execution stage and start eating their victim alive.

RAPID DEATH

In practice this is not as appalling as it sounds, because the weakness of their long jaws forces them to attack the softest part of their prey: the underbelly. They rip out its entrails, and the shock of this, coupled with the massive loss of blood, is often enough to kill the animal almost instantly. A small animal like a Thomson's gazelle is usually dead within seconds of being pulled down, and an impala or young wildebeest—the largest prey taken regularly by wild dogs—succumbs almost as quickly. It is only the big, powerful animals such as adult wildebeest and zebra that take several minutes to die, particularly if the pack is small. However, trying to eat a big, struggling animal is inconvenient and potentially suicidal, so wild dogs tend to concentrate on easier targets unless the pack is big enough to ensure a quick kill. ∎

A hungry pup licks its mother's muzzle, hoping that she will regurgitate a softened meal of meat.

HABITATS

Wild dogs are always associated with the grassy savannas of tropical Africa, but this image has more to do with the distribution of zoologists and wildlife film crews than of the dogs themselves. The open plains offer the best opportunities for watching and filming the dogs in action, because the terrain is ideal for off-road vehicles and there is little cover for the animals. Inevitably this means that nearly all the data we have on the African wild dog have been collected on the open grasslands, but they are misleading.

Until recently the wild dog was widespread across Africa, south of the Sahara, occurring in every type of habitat except tropical rain forest. Dog packs can survive in marginal habitats such as swamplands and semidesert, and a pack of five dogs was once sighted on the permanent snow on the summit of Mount Kilimanjaro, 19,337 ft (5,894 m) above sea level. Wild dogs still roam the arid landscapes of the Kalahari in southern Africa, as well as the dense upland forests of the Bale Mountains in Ethiopia, but their preferred habitat is probably savanna woodland and scrub, where their coats provide superb camouflage.

SCRUB HUNTERS

Most pack dogs are scrub hunters at heart. The scrub cover provides plenty of scope for outflanking fleeing prey, and both the wolf and the dhole, one of the African wild dog's nearest relatives, are adept at hunting in dense forest. In Africa, however, the lure of the great herds grazing the plains has drawn the dog out onto the open savanna, and it has adapted remarkably well. It can outrun its prey in a straight chase across open terrain, and can cope well with the heat. Its outsized ears are well supplied with

> AS LATE AS 1970 THE WILD DOG WAS
> STILL WIDESPREAD ACROSS AFRICA,
> SOUTH OF THE SAHARA

thin-walled blood vessels that dissipate excess body heat. It can also let its body temperature rise well above the optimum before it begins heavy panting—a valuable moisture-conserving device that enables wild dogs in the Kalahari to survive for months without access to drinking water. In such habitats the dogs get all the water they need from the body fluids of their prey. Wild dogs have also adapted their behavior, confining most of their hunting activity to the cooler hours of the day. They may hunt at night, although since they hunt mainly by sight, they normally save such nocturnal forays for nights when the moon is full.

FOCUS ON

Wild dogs are no longer found in South Africa; this adult in Botswana is on the fringes of its range.

But simply being equipped for chasing prey on the open grasslands is no guarantee of success, because in some areas the prey has a habit of vanishing overnight. The plains of the Serengeti–Mara ecosystem are famous for this phenomenon. From December to May, in the rainy season, the Rift Valley grasslands in the southeast of the Serengeti National Park support vast herds of antelope, zebra, and gazelle, but when the rain ceases, the grass stops growing and the food supply soon dwindles. The animals start to leave, and by May the movement has escalated into a full-scale migration as the herds trek northwest to the grazing near Seronera, in the center of the national park. They remain there for two or three months until they have grazed the vegetation to the ground, then head off northeast to the Masai Mara, over the border in Kenya, where the grass is still green. They stay here until November, when the onset of the rainy season sends them south again to the southern Serengeti.

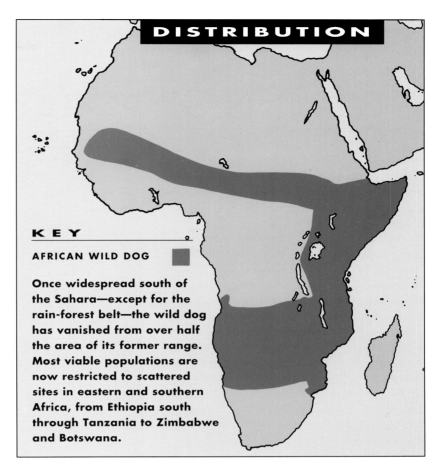

DISTRIBUTION

KEY

AFRICAN WILD DOG ▪

Once widespread south of the Sahara—except for the rain-forest belt—the wild dog has vanished from over half the area of its former range. Most viable populations are now restricted to scattered sites in eastern and southern Africa, from Ethiopia south through Tanzania to Zimbabwe and Botswana.

THE MASAI MARA

The wooded grasslands of the Masai Mara in Kenya lie to the north of the Serengeti National Park in Tanzania, and form part of the same ecosystem. A large part of the area is a nature preserve, and much of the remainder is maintained in its natural state as grazing land for the cattle of the local Masai tribe. It is a richer landscape than much of the Serengeti, and supports Thomson's gazelle and other medium-sized herbivores throughout the year as well as great herds of wildebeest during the dry season. Despite this, there are relatively few lions and hyenas, and this combination of plentiful prey and reduced competition makes the region ideal for wild dogs. In recent years it has been one of the few places in Africa where they can live and hunt in large packs, and it has given scientists new insights into the natural behavior of wild dogs.

Yet although the Mara is ideal for wild dogs, it can support only one or two packs at a time, in the north of the nature preserve. Here they cross paths with the Masai herders and their dogs. The Masai themselves have no argument with the wild dogs—which never attack their cattle while wild game exists—but the domestic dogs carry deadly diseases. In 1989 the resident Mara pack was wiped out by disease, and it could happen again.

Such migrations affect wild dogs in different ways, depending on the habitat. In semiarid grassland the dry season creates a prey famine, and the dogs must roam over huge areas to find food. They may follow the herds on their migratory treks, but as they do so, they may trespass on the home range of a neighboring dog pack, if there is one. As far as we know, wild dogs are not jealously territorial and the home ranges of neighboring packs often overlap. Nevertheless, the dogs tend to remain in a particular area throughout the year, and simply hunt over a wider area when prey is scarce.

In richer habitats, such as the Masai Mara, there are plenty of small grazing animals that remain on the grasslands throughout the year—even after the larger migrants have gone—and the wild dogs can get all they need within a smaller area. Such habitats can potentially support several large dog packs, enabling good hunting, social interaction, and the interbreeding that is vital to the long-term survival of any species. By contrast, dogs living in seasonally impoverished habitats generally live in small, scattered groups. Such groups are often barely viable as packs, being unable to defend their kills or their pups against marauding lions and hyenas, and as a result they often fail to breed successfully and their numbers dwindle still further. So although wild dogs can survive in areas where prey is scarce, they cannot thrive in the same way as less social species. They need rich pickings or a lot of space, and today both commodities are in short supply. ▪

HUNTING

The African wild dog is one of the most social of all canids. Wolves typically live in packs, but a wolf may wander off and hunt alone for weeks with adequate success. By contrast, a wild dog is virtually incapable of surviving by itself.

This is partly for practical reasons: As a specialist at hunting cooperatively for relatively large prey, it is at a disadvantage if it is forced to rely on its own resources. But there are more subtle psychological factors involved. Wild dogs are compulsively gregarious: They seem lost without companionship. Dog packs are often far larger than is necessary for effective hunting—for there is a limit to the number of dogs that can mount an attack on one animal, even a powerful beast like a zebra. Other canids like foxes show a similar taste for living in company even though they typically hunt alone, and this suggests that the social instinct of ancestral wild dogs was well developed long before they began to hunt together for large animals. The social bond forms the foundation for the hunting pack—it is not something that develops because the dogs find it useful to hunt together. Nonetheless, in the case of the wild dog, social habits and cooperative hunting strategies are now inextricably linked together.

Hunting as a large group has certain hidden advantages. Each kill may involve only a few dogs at a time, but defending the kill can be a different matter. Lions and hyenas are always on the lookout for easy pickings, since by stealing another predator's prey, they avoid burning energy in a protracted hunt. A small pack of dogs may be able to kill a medium-sized antelope without much trouble, but

A wildebeest is subdued by the highly effective lip-hold technique (above). *Once a wild dog gets such a grip, the fight is all but over.*

EASY MEAT
The less experienced among the pack will have no trouble in dispatching this wildebeest calf (above) *now that it is cut off from its mother.*

Jonathan Scott/Planet Earth Pictures

DOGS OF WAR

Surrounded by excited pack members, the key killers go to work to poleax their prey (below). *As soon as the victim hits the ground, they will disembowel it.*

they have no hope of defending it against a pride of lions or a twenty-strong hyena clan. On the open plains, in particular, it is very difficult for large predators to hunt inconspicuously; if nothing else, the circling vultures soon alert other carnivores to the chance of a free meal. For these reasons, wild dogs very rarely return to an earlier kill, and seldom bother to cache any surplus meat—chances are that another predator or scavenger will find the booty first. Speed is the secret. Wild dogs have learned to gobble down their fill before the competition arrives—they never waste time fighting over the spoils as lions do—but it is even better to keep the scavengers at bay by sheer force of numbers. Today wild dogs rarely live in packs that are sufficiently large to achieve this, and their inability to defend their prey is a factor in their continuing decline.

Many canids, particularly foxes, hunt small, elusive prey. They use their finely tuned senses and stalking skills to locate and creep close to their victims before pouncing on them and killing them with a single bite. They are well adapted for this style of hunting, with acute senses of smell and hearing, lightweight agile bodies, and just enough jaw power to effect a clean kill. This, in a sense, is what dogs are designed for.

GROUP BENEFITS

Such a hunting style, however, is almost completely alien to the African wild dog. A young wild dog may stalk and kill hares, but only for practice. An adult may snap up a cane rat if it comes across one, but it rarely wastes time searching out and stalking one.

For example, six wild dogs weighing 55 lb (25 kg) apiece can easily kill an adult female wildebeest weighing over 330 lb (150 kg), providing each with its own weight in prey. Hunting alone, each dog would have to kill five savanna hares weighing maybe 10 lb (4.5 kg) each to achieve the same result—but at roughly five times the energy expense. So although wild dogs have retained the features that make dogs in general such accomplished hunters of small game, they have developed a completely different hunting strategy. Instead of seeking out creatures that are hard to find but easy to kill, they concentrate on animals that are easy to find

SECURE DELIVERY

One of the main problems faced by wild dogs is prey piracy. A small pack of dogs may achieve a kill only to have it stolen from them by hyenas, and a single dog carrying meat back to the breeding den would be lucky to complete the journey with its burden intact.

This is one very good reason why wild dogs swallow meat intended for the pups, carry it back to the den in their stomachs, and regurgitate it on demand. The habit may seem rather revolting to us, but it certainly guarantees secure delivery of the food supplies that are vital to the survival of both the pups and their mother.

Illustration Peter David Scott/Wildlife Art Agency

but hard to kill. To achieve this, they must pool their resources, not only to outmaneuver and overwhelm their prey but also to defend their prize from more powerful predators. They must hunt in packs.

Locating prey is easy enough on the African plains, for although the grazing herds may not be near at hand, they are conspicuous. But zebras are big, powerful animals, and few wild dogs are prepared to tackle them. What the dogs seek, typically, are smaller animals like Thomson's and Grant's gazelles, impala, reedbuck, lechwe, and springbok, as well as young and immature wildebeest.

Where conditions are favorable, wild dogs tend to go for the most common species in any single area. In a study conducted in South Africa's Kruger National Park, for example, where impala outnumbered every other species, this species was prominent in nearly 90 percent of 2,745 dog kills. But wild dogs are not fussy: In Kafue National Park in south-central Zambia, where animals in the dogs' favored size range were less abundant, more than a dozen species appeared in one pack's diet. In the Serengeti ecosystem, Thomson's gazelles are high on the menu, although the dogs switch to wildebeest calves after the birth peak in February. They will also take mature wildebeest if they get the chance, although they rarely attack healthy, unencumbered adults. Like most predators they select weak, old, or injured animals and the stragglers. To do this they employ a simple test: They get them running.

Jonathan Scott/Planet Earth Pictures

There is no particular subtlety about a typical wild dog hunt on the open savanna. The pack members keep a low profile until they get reasonably close to their prey, bunching to reduce their apparent numbers and crouching low with ears pinned back, but once they are within range, they just charge. The ensuing panic soon reveals the easy targets to the more experienced dogs, which veer off in pursuit. If the pack is big enough—or the prey is small enough—the dogs may split up to pursue several animals at once, but if the prey is going to take all their combined weight to bring down, they tend to stream after the leader's choice. They run and run, effortlessly, driving their quarry on until it begins to flag.

This family feeding frenzy is typical of wild dogs (above): *There is no time to waste in squabbling over prey when there are pups to feed.*

Brian Edwards/Wildlife Art Agency

ACT OF PIRACY

If you can't kill your own zebra, steal one! When pushed, a wild dog pack will pluck up the nerve to drive an isolated lion from its kill (below).

This is when the individual skills of the dogs become apparent. A particularly fast dog—often a female—races forward to outflank the fugitive. A strong young male—often, somewhat surprisingly, the alpha leader's mate—risks a shattered skull by flinging itself at the animal's tail or hind leg to slow it down while another particularly skilled, agile hunter overhauls the animal and leaps at its head to grab its upper lip. If it succeeds, the race is over. The lip hold has an almost paralyzing effect on the victim—indeed, some studies suggest that it triggers the release of a powerful natural sedative (an endorphin) that both immobilizes the animal and acts as an anesthetic. If so, then it is a merciful deliverance, for once their victim is brought down, the whole pack piles in and starts to rip it apart. They tear out its innards, eating fast—for there are always other, bigger predators on the lookout for an easy meal. Each dog bolts down as much as it can, both for its own nutrition and, in the breeding season, to be regurgitated to any pups back at the den. Any remains may be carried away, but all too often they have to be surrendered to lions and scavenging hyenas.

Once the wild dogs have a victim on the run, its chances of survival are slim, but this does not mean that the prey species are defenseless. All potential prey animals can avoid being singled out by sticking with the herd and demonstrating how fit they are as the dogs move in. Several species of gazelle take this principle to extremes by leaping high in the air as they make their getaway—a behavior known as stotting or pronking—to show the predators they are wasting their time pursuing such agile quarry. And if psychology fails, there is always violence. A zebra stallion can kill a dog with a well-aimed kick. Antelope have sharp horns and hoofs, and a bachelor

SINCE THEY CANNOT HIDE ON THE OPEN PLAINS, PREY ANIMALS RELY ON SAFETY IN NUMBERS TO ESCAPE PREDATORS

herd of bull wildebeest can easily hold their own. Even the smaller females can inflict severe damage on wild dogs, and often do so in defense of their calves. A wild dog is no heavyweight killer, like a lion, and if it makes an error of judgment, it is likely to be brushed aside and fatally injured. It says something for the dogs' intelligence, therefore, that their success rate is phenomenal. Some packs achieve a kill in nine out of every ten attempts, indicating a great skill in assessing their targets. Considering their evolutionary origins as stealthy hunters of small game, it is a remarkable achievement.

LEARNING THE ROPES

Social skills are not only crucial during the chase itself; there is evidence, culled from recent studies conducted on the Serengeti, that some wild dog packs have passed down specialized hunting traditions through successive generations. Out of ten dog packs studied as they hunted over the plains, two achieved regular success in tackling and killing zebras—a spectacular feat, considering the difficulty normally encountered in bringing down a single such animal. The zebra-killing packs were no larger than other, less ambitious packs—they contained eight adults or so each—so their secret clearly did not lie in sheer weight of numbers, nor was their preference due simply to a lack of easier targets.

It seems instead that, once having mastered the art of hunting zebra, each generation was keen to pass it on; perhaps it is feasible that the pack recognized a niche currently exploited only by big cats. Wild dogs also pass on other pack lore through the generations: where to find water and shelter, locations for good hunting—all are typical examples of canid cunning. ■

615

SOCIAL STRUCTURE

Each wild dog pack is an extended family, potentially comprising a breeding pair, their unmated brothers and sisters, and their young from several years. All the adults help care for the new season's pups, guarding them in the den and bringing food; most of these helpers are male, and quite often there is only one adult female in the pack—the mother of all the others.

KEEP IT IN THE FAMILY

This is possible because wild dogs give birth to huge litters of sixteen or more pups—enough to form a pack in their own right. Two or three seasons of breeding at this rate could create an army of wild dogs, all sharing the same mother. But the breeding, or "alpha," female cannot possibly feed her huge litter by her own efforts, so she enlists the help of their grown relations. Since these are full siblings of the pups, they have a strong interest in their survival and willingly help at the breeding den until tension mounts or opportunity to break away presents itself.

Breeding by subordinate females works to the disadvantage of the matriarch of the pack—the alpha female. Various behavioral and other mechanisms appear to inhibit breeding in associated females, although exceptions do occur. When this happens, the resulting tension between the two breeding females can erupt into violence, especially if food is scarce, and subordinate females are often driven away. But the alpha female cannot risk losing all her helpers, so she may encourage the males to stay at home by letting them mate with her. These dalliances are restricted mainly to the period just before the female ovulates, so she is unlikely to become pregnant, and they occur with the full knowledge of the dominant male.

The upshot of this is a society in which females leave the pack while males tend to stay at home. Males also leave, particularly if the pack grows to the point where low-ranking brothers have little to gain by staying, and if they do disperse, they often travel much further than females. But the higher-ranking males are unlikely to abandon their advantages. The most senior apart from the alpha male are his own brothers, who may have emigrated with him from their own natal pack, and consequently many wild dog packs revolve around a tight partnership of the alpha male, his brothers, and his mate.

EMIGRANTS

Emigrating dogs nearly always leave in groups of at least three so that they can hunt effectively. The travelers soon sort out a hierarchy, and if they meet up with another group of the opposite sex, the leaders are likely to pair up. Some of the male's brothers may stay with the pair, but the female generally starts to squabble with her sisters, and this leads them to leave again. A few extra males may join the party, and so create a new pack. One male teams up with the senior female to create a new alpha pair, and the other females get restless again.

FAMILY FUN

Tensions within the pack rise to breaking point when members leave, others join, and subordinate females breed out of turn. But at almost all other times, life is peaceful in this intricately structured society, and the family members delight in each other's company (below).

One consequence of this arrangement is that unlucky females undergo a kind of serial dispersal, moving from pack to pack in search of the status that will allow them to breed. Since dispersal is the most dangerous time of any adult animal's life, the death rate among females is correspondingly high, and, on average, males outnumber females by two to one. Clearly females have a lot to gain from reaching high status in the pack, and as a result they can compete aggressively with each other for the right to breed. Their brothers are more relaxed, and serious fights between rival males are rare.

Once the hierarchy is sorted, the pack tends to settle down to a quiet life, for, in general, wild dogs enjoy each other's company immensely. The dominant pair nearly always rest together, often in close

ON THE ROAD

Subordinate females— and, to a degree, males—soon get bored living in a pack that denies them the right to breed, so they leave to form their own pack. But life is hard for these exiles, who all too often lose their kills to hyenas (above) *and other tough neighbors.*

physical contact, and all the members of the pack greet each other extravagantly at every opportunity. The subordinates appease their superiors with infantile behavior that may win them privileges they would otherwise not enjoy: Pups generally get precedence at kills and benefit from the indulgent behavior of their elders, so by imitating them, a subordinate adult may gain similar treats. Each morning and evening, before setting out to hunt, group members indulge in a ritual reaffirmation of their relationship, licking each other's faces and squirming their bodies together in an ecstatic celebration of the ties that bind them together—the bond that makes them so devastating as a hunting pack. ■

LEADER OF THE PACK

The qualities that make a pack leader are hard to define. Males and females have separate hierarchies, so they do not have to compete with each other, but all the evidence suggests that they achieve dominance by their success at the same skill—hunting.

An alpha male may be a particularly resolute individual, prepared to brave the flailing hoofs of fleeing prey when the others hang back. A female may be very fast, or skilled at outmaneuvering gazelles as they attempt to zigzag their way out of trouble. Either way, they win the respect of their packmates, and may retain it long after younger animals have started to outperform them in the chase.

LIFE CYCLE

Many wild dog packs spend most of the year roaming in search of prey, but they cannot breed on the move, since the pups need the shelter of a secure den. This limits the hunting scope of the pack just when they need to be most certain of their food supply, so they must choose the right time and place. Packs breed in response to local conditions, so in areas where prey animals migrate, the dog packs in each area will breed at different times.

When a female comes into heat, she quickly attracts the attention of the males. Junior males may mate with her before she ovulates, but the dominant male usually fathers the pups, attending the female closely during her fertile period and denying the others access to her. At 70–75 days, the gestation is the longest known among dogs, but for two-thirds of this period the fetuses remain small, only growing rapidly during the final three or four weeks of the pregnancy. This enables the female to stay active for as long as possible before she dens.

BRINGING UP THE PUPS

A typical breeding den is a burrow dug and abandoned by some other animal, such as an aardvark or a hyena, deep enough to maintain a stable temperature. After the pups are born, the mother spends the first few days with them in the den, and even when she emerges, she stays nearby while the rest of the pack hunt. The adults bring her food, regurgitating it on demand, and when the pups start to take solid food at the age of three to four weeks, they bring meat for them, too. Both mother and pups rely on the other adults to keep them supplied, and it is doubtful whether a breeding pair on their own would be able to raise a litter to maturity. From about seven weeks subordinate adults may stay at the den to guard the pups while the mother hunts with the rest of the pack, and these helpers beg food alongside the pups.

At about two months old the pups begin to acquire their rangy adult shape and coloration. Their games become more earnest as they start to sort out who's who, and they begin tagging along behind the pack as it sets off to hunt. Initially an adult may lead them back to the den, but in time they are allowed to feed directly from the kill. The adults always move aside to allow the pups to feed, although they take care to eat as much as possible before the pups catch up. At about ten weeks the pack abandons the den and returns to the nomadic life, but it will be several months before the young recruits learn the art of hunting for themselves.

COMING OUT

When the pups are three or four weeks old, their mother forsakes the den and starts to suckle them outside (above).

FROM BIRTH TO DEATH

AFRICAN WILD DOG

GESTATION: 70–75 DAYS
LITTER SIZE: 2–19, AVERAGE 7–10
BREEDING: MATE WHEN PREY BECOMES SEASONALLY ABUNDANT
WEIGHT AT BIRTH: 14 OZ (400 G)
EYES OPEN: 3 WEEKS
FIRST LEAVE DEN: 3–4 WEEKS
HUNTING WITH PACK: 12–14 MONTHS
SEXUAL MATURITY: 12–18 MONTHS
LONGEVITY: RARELY UP TO 10 YEARS

Illustration Carol Roberts

PULLING RANK

Like all the pack, the pups receive their fair share of a kill, after which the alpha female will readily steal the surplus from their mouths (above).

618

GROWING UP

The life of an African wild pup

FEED ME

By about five weeks old the pups are begging food from all the adults in the pack. The adults respond tolerantly enough, often playing with the pups and allowing them all kinds of liberties.

A HUMBLE ACT

The pups incite adults to bring up food by licking at their lips (left). This act becomes central to the dogs' social life, with juniors using it as a gesture of submission to their superiors.

ⓘ SIGHT

FAMILY PLANNING

Occasionally a wild dog pack will rear two litters at once. If prey is abundant, there is less pressure to concentrate the whole pack's resources on one litter, and the alpha female may tolerate breeding by one of the subordinate females. More usually, though, the harsh economics of life in the wild dictate otherwise, and if a subordinate produces pups, they are quite likely to be killed and even eaten by the alpha female.

Luckily such extreme measures are rarely necessary, for subordinate females seem to have their breeding instincts suppressed while they remain under the influence of the alpha female. It may be that psychological pressure leads to a reduction in hormone levels, preventing ovulation; alternatively there may be some chemical factor, possibly in the dominant female's urine. Either way, the alpha female usually gets her way.

TUG-OF-WAR

The alpha female wrestles a pup from a younger mother who has also bred a litter (below).

619

CATASTROPHIC DECLINE

BADLY HIT BY THE EROSION OF THEIR WILD HABITATS AND THE DECLINE OF THEIR PREY, THE DWINDLING, SCATTERED WILD DOG PACKS ARE BESET BY THE THREATS OF PERSECUTION, STARVATION, AND DISEASE

Wild dogs are very rare. In the whole of the Serengeti–Mara ecosystem there are usually only one to six viable packs of wild dogs flourishing at any one time: a total of perhaps 80 adults and pups, at most. Recently, through disease, this figure has crashed to less than 10. In the whole of Africa there may be no more than 4,000–6,000 in total.

As a species, the African wild dog has probably never been common. Large predators never are, and the wild dog's tendency to roam over huge areas on a regular basis has always ensured that the packs were well spaced out. But in the past each pack tended to be much bigger. Packs with 100 or more adult members were being reported a century ago; Karen Blixen, the author of *Out of Africa*, described a single group of about 500 dogs hunting together in the Masai country. Today most packs have fewer than 10 adults, plus pups. Many packs have shrunk into extinction, and since the 1980s the wild dog has gone from 25 of the 32 African countries that once had viable populations. The rate of decline has been catastrophic: In the mid-1980s, when the species was first classified as endangered by the International Union for the Conservation of Nature (IUCN), its numbers were estimated at 10,000. Ten years later this figure had been halved. A survey in Zimbabwe found that the wild dog population had shriveled by 99 percent in five years. It seems likely that unless something quite extraordinary happens, the species could be close to extinction by the end of the 20th century.

HATED AND HOUNDED

The basic reason for this spectacular collapse is the familiar combination of persecution and habitat destruction, coupled with an unusual vulnerability

Pups beg for food—a resource that, today, is becoming ever more scarce for the dogs (below).

Jonathan Scott/Planet Earth Pictures

Jonathan Scott/Planet Earth Pictures

*When pack sizes dwindle below a critical size,
hunting becomes impossible and the dogs starve.*

Rabies (below) *can sweep like wildfire through
even the strongest of wild dog packs.*

Jonathan Scott/Planet Earth Pictures

to disease. Ever since Europeans arrived in Africa,
the wild dog has been regarded as a peculiarly vile
form of vermin. Loathed for its apparently vicious
nature and cruel killing methods, it was also feared
as a potential threat to livestock and humans—a fear
that was almost certainly groundless, since Masai
herders have been grazing their livestock in wild dog
country for centuries without trouble. Since it was
not even credited with the dignity of being a worthy
target for big-game hunters—unlike the lion—there
was absolutely no reason to keep it alive, so it was
eradicated using every means available.

This philosophy even extended to the great
African wildlife preserves, where it was once common practice to shoot wild dogs on sight. This
astonishing policy had its roots in the prejudice against
dogs, but it was justified by the gamekeeper tradition
of wildlife management, in which predators are seen
as a threat to the welfare of the other animals. It was
not until the mid-1960s that wiser advice prevailed,

following research demonstrating that the predators actually improved the condition of the herds by taking out the weak and diseased individuals. Today the wild dog is protected within the preserve areas, but unfortunately its wide-ranging habits often take it far beyond the preserve boundaries, with occasionally fatal results. In 1988 a South African farmer with land bordering the Kruger National Park shot 20 dogs encroaching on his property, wiping out 10 percent of the park's total population.

DWINDLING PREY

Direct persecution is the most obvious threat to any wild animal, but it is rarely the most serious. In the case of the wild dog, the breeding potential of the species would probably have enabled it to absorb such losses, all other things being equal. But unfortunately, while the farmers were shooting wild dogs they were dealing out the same treatment to their prey—the antelope, gazelle, zebra, and wild cattle that once grazed the African plains in their millions. Within a century of the European colonization of South Africa most of these great grazing herds had disappeared—either shot for sport or to make way for the colonists' cattle—and the wild grasslands

TODAY A PACK OF 100 WILD DOGS SIMPLY COULD NOT OPERATE: IT WOULD EXHAUST ITS FOOD SUPPLY IN JUST A FEW WEEKS

were being fenced off and plowed up. The surviving wild animals were pushed back to the game preserves and wildernesses, where their shrunken populations cannot sustain the large numbers of carnivores that had once preyed on them.

ROAMING NO MORE

The erosion of natural habitats in Africa still goes on. The relentless increase in the human population creates an insatiable demand for farmland, firewood, bushmeat (wild animals trapped and butchered for sale in local markets), and other natural resources. Where the wildlife preserves were once areas delineated on the map, but in practice barely distinguishable from the surrounding landscape, they are now increasingly hemmed in by ranching and cropland, which effectively isolates them from other areas of natural habitat.

This affects different species in different ways. Some animals seem able to thrive within the confines of the preserves, so although their numbers have dwindled compared to their former abundance, they survive in flourishing local populations. The spotted hyena, for example—an animal with a lifestyle not unlike that of the wild dog—still lives in

Jonathan Scott/Planet Earth Pictures

ENDANGERED SPECIES

ENEMIES FROM WITHIN

Wild dogs have many enemies, but the most insidious of these are the microorganisms that infect them with lethal diseases. Many flourishing packs have been destroyed by disease over the past few decades, and it is only recently that scientists have made a serious effort to identify the infections responsible.

For years it was assumed that the dogs were dying of canine distemper, which first appeared among domestic dogs in Africa at the beginning of the century. Wild dogs regularly come into contact with domestic dogs, so they have ample opportunity to contract infections. If the problem could be narrowed down to one particular disease, there might be a chance of eliminating it by vaccination, for a similar campaign succeeded in eliminating cattle plague, or rinderpest, from wild and domestic grazing animals in and around the Serengeti preserve in the 1950s.

Unfortunately the problem is more complex. Wild dogs are prone to a variety of diseases, many of which superficially resemble distemper, and the only way of identifying the actual disease is to test blood samples from infected dogs. Such samples cannot be simply screened for any foreign bodies—they have to be tested for antibodies to each possible disease in turn—and so far the results have been inconclusive. On one occasion a test for

CONSERVATION MEASURES

• In 1987 Dr. Pieter Kat, a geneticist at the Nairobi Museum, initiated a study into the wild dogs in Kenya, with emphasis on the disease problem. The study has involved scientists all over the world in an effort to isolate the cause of the wild dog decline.

• It is possible to protect domestic dogs from distemper, parvovirus, leptosporosis, and hepatitis with one inoculation, but any such

rabies proved positive, but a sample taken from another wild dog that had died in similar circumstances tested negative.

Whatever the actual nature of the disease, its effect on any dog pack is bound to be catastrophic. The intimate nature of wild dog society ensures that any dog that becomes infected passes on the disease almost immediately. Healthy dogs have been seen licking their dying packmates in the mouth in an attempt to rouse them from their lethargy—an action that could hardly be more efficient as a way of transmitting disease. As one vet has pointed out, "From the point of view of disease, a pack of dogs is one animal."

THE WILD DOG IN DANGER

THE INTERNATIONAL UNION FOR THE CONSERVATION OF NATURE (IUCN), OR THE WORLD CONSERVATION UNION, NOW CLASSIFIES THE STATUS OF THE AFRICAN WILD DOG AS *ENDANGERED*—WHICH MEANS THAT THE SPECIES IS FACING A VERY HIGH PROBABILITY OF EXTINCTION IN THE NEAR FUTURE IF NOTHING IS DONE TO IMPROVE ITS SITUATION:

AFRICAN WILD DOG	ENDANGERED

ACCORDING TO THE MOST RECENT REPORT, THE WILD DOG RANGES WIDELY OVER AFRICA, BUT ITS SUB-SAHARAN POPULATIONS, AND THOSE IN THE HORN OF AFRICA, ARE SEVERELY THREATENED. VIABLE POPULATIONS PROBABLY EXIST ONLY IN EASTERN AND SOUTHERN COUNTRIES NORTH OF SOUTH AFRICA.

Peter Pickford/NHPA

UNLESS RADICAL STEPS ARE TAKEN TO SAVE THEM, PACKS SUCH AS THESE MAY SOON BECOME HISTORY.

program carried out among wild dogs would have to be repeated annually to cope with the uptake of youngsters into the pack.

• The rabies problem among foxes in Europe is being solved by distributing bait laced with a new oral vaccine. The same method might work in Africa, for although wild dogs rarely take carrion, other potentially infectious species do.

large, self-regenerating clans. As a result there are some 3,000–4,000 spotted hyenas within the Serengeti, compared with a handful of wild dogs. It seems that the dogs cannot thrive unless they have vast areas of landscape to roam over, although the reasons for this are still not clear.

The other problem afflicting wild dogs is their vulnerability to disease. Canids in general are notoriously prone to a variety of potentially lethal infections including rabies, distemper, anthrax, parvovirus, and a variety of tick-borne diseases, and African wild dogs seem to be more susceptible than most. Many packs have been wiped out by disease in recent years, although the actual nature of the diseases involved is still uncertain.

COMPETING CARNIVORES

One thing is quite clear. Wild dogs are extremely social, and as their numbers decline and the packs get smaller, for whatever reason, their cooperative way of life begins to break down. The most dramatic demonstration of this is their inability to defend their kills from other carnivores. A small pack may be able to make a kill—expending a lot of energy in the process—but it is likely to have it carried away by hyenas or lions within minutes. Driven to desperation, the dogs may fight back, with disastrous results. Heavyweight carnivores such as lions can toss a dog in the air like a rag doll and kill it with a single bite, and a spotted hyena is considerably bigger and more powerful than a wild dog. These animals will also kill and eat wild dog pups if they get the chance; the smaller the pack, the more opportunities they get.

The tendency to take more risks extends to the hunt itself: A hungry dog may be badly injured if it launches an ill-judged strike at an animal that it has no hope of subduing without the backup of a healthy

ALONGSIDE MAN

RELIABLE PERFORMERS

Although most people still view the hunting methods of African wild dogs with mixed feelings, there is no denying the excitement of watching such magnificent predators in action. Recently, tour operators in the African wildlife preserves have begun to value wild dog packs as dependable attractions in a land where many of the more spectacular predators hunt by night. Lions tend to spend most of the day dozing in the shade, while leopards are simply too elusive. Only cheetahs and wild dogs can reliably provide the kind of spine-tingling spectacle that high-paying visitors to the safari camps have been led to expect.

As a result, the rangers have become skilled at locating and monitoring the now-scarce dog packs. The dogs themselves seem unperturbed by their audience, so they can probably only gain from the attention. A steady flow of satisfied visitors to the wildlife preserves ensures a steady flow of hard currency into the national coffers, and if the wild dogs are recognized as a contributory factor, the local authorities may do more to secure their survival. Although several African countries have lost almost all their wild dogs, they are still to be seen on preserves in the Serengeti and Masai Mara.

pack. Indeed, there is evidence that solitary survivors of defunct packs may not bother to hunt, but simply starve to death. Hunting would probably just accelerate the process, since the dog would waste valuable energy in the pursuit of prey only to see it stolen by other predators.

Other canids such as wolves might survive in such a situation by turning to smaller prey and scraps, but wild dogs may be reluctant to do this. They are highly specialized pack hunters, conditioned to work as a group, and on the open savannas, at any rate, most of the available prey demands the cooperative approach that they have brought to such a pitch of refinement. In scrub country and woodland there is more scope for private enterprise, but the dogs would still prefer to hunt in packs. Ultimately mere survival is not enough: The dogs must breed and multiply, and to do this each mated pair needs the help of other adults working together for the good of the pups. As pack sizes decline, the chances of breeding successfully decline too, and the resulting downward spiral may have only one disastrous outcome. ∎

Shoot to thrill: A photographer on safari captures the more mischievous side to these canids.

David Cayless/Oxford Scientific Films

INTO THE FUTURE

Despite its steep decline over the last century, the African wild dog may yet recover. If a pack has sufficient adult members and plenty of prey, it can multiply rapidly, doubling or even tripling its numbers each year.

In late 1985, for example, a pack of nine adult wild dogs settled near Aitong Hill to the north of the Masai Mara preserve—long known as a favored denning area—and flourished for three generations. Unusually for wild dogs, both the dominant female and her sister bred within the pack for several successive seasons, raising their pups side by side. In 1986, 17 pups were born to the two females, 11 of which eventually moved away. In 1987 the sisters produced 18 pups, 13 of which dispersed. In 1988 they bore 22 pups between them, making a total of 57 recruits generated by the original 9-strong pack—a 7-fold increase over three seasons.

PREDICTION

THREATS REMAIN UNCHALLENGED

Increasing interest in this dog will ensure that its decline is well documented, but unless a real breakthrough is made soon, the decline will continue. Its main hope lies in keeping established populations free from diseases such as rabies.

But then disaster struck. In September 1989 an outbreak of disease, subsequently identified as rabies, killed all the adults and 17 of the yearlings. Of the Aitong pack only 2 yearling males survived. Yet over the years at least 25 young dogs had dispersed away from the area and survived, so despite the rabies outbreak, the original pack of 9 had managed to triple its numbers.

It seems likely that the wild dog developed this prolific breeding capacity as a way of building up numbers after periods of high mortality—through either food shortage, predation, or disease—and that this boom-bust pattern is a natural feature of its ecology. Up on the tundra the arctic fox employs this strategy to weather periodic prey shortages, and it is the only other canid capable of matching the wild dog's birthrate. So if the zoologists working on behalf of the wild dog can only find ways of reducing the scale of mortality, the wild dog may yet be able to breed its way out of trouble. ■

SATELLITE TRACKING

There are now wild dog projects under way in several African countries, employing the latest technology to monitor dog populations and trace the movements of individual packs. One of the main problems associated with such studies in the past was the extreme difficulty of keeping track of animals that range over such huge distances, often crossing national boundaries, but this obstacle has now been reduced by the use of satellite tracking.

Conventional radio tracking has been employed in wild dog studies for several years, using miniature transmitters attached to dog collars, but it has its drawbacks. The VHF radio signals emitted by each transmitter travel in straight lines, and are therefore screened if the animal moves over the horizon or behind a hill. Monitoring the signals from airplanes or helicopters is a partial solution, but this does not allow dog movements to be kept under constant surveillance.

Satellite tracking is different. Already proven to be successful even with sea mammals such as elephant seals, it uses the technology employed by the navigation computers on ships and aircraft to locate suitably equipped dogs to the nearest 330 feet (100 meters), wherever they may be. In one such study, the position "fixes" are relayed through space to a computer in France three times a day to provide a continuously updated map of the dogs' movements. By such modern means we may yet learn a lot about the African wild dog.

Illustration Evi Antoniou

DOLPHINS

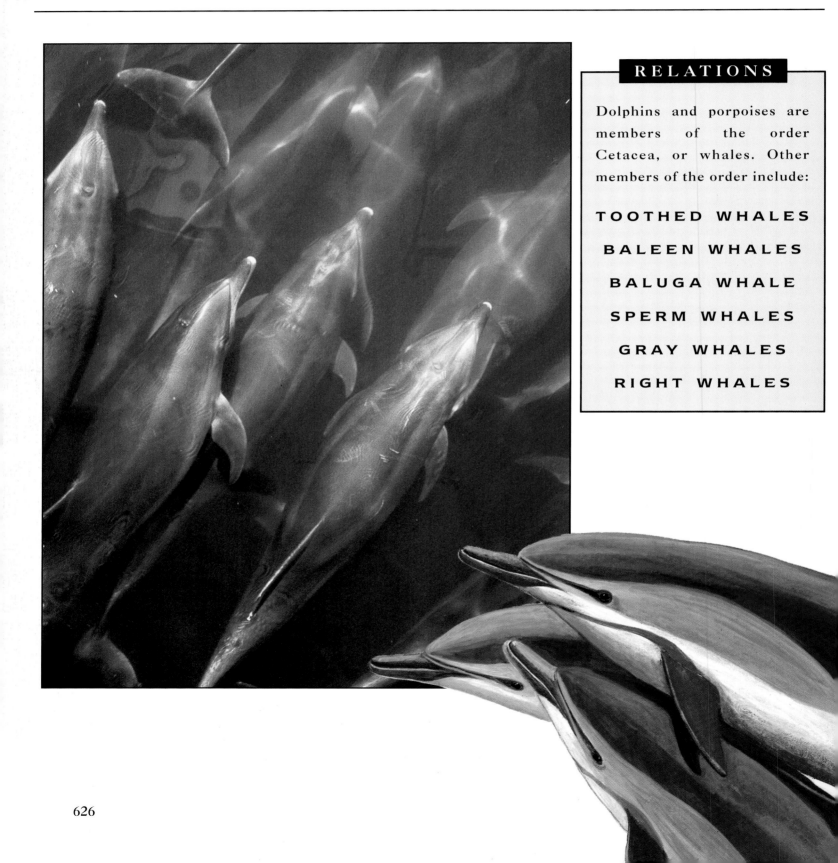

RELATIONS

Dolphins and porpoises are members of the order Cetacea, or whales. Other members of the order include:

TOOTHED WHALES

BALEEN WHALES

BALUGA WHALE

SPERM WHALES

GRAY WHALES

RIGHT WHALES

Jim Watt/ZEFA

STREAMLINED SWIMMERS

WITH THEIR PERFECTLY STREAMLINED BODIES POWERED BY STRONG, BROAD TAILS, DOLPHINS SLIP EASILY THROUGH OCEAN OR RIVER

T he bottle-nosed dolphin *(above)*, with its smiling face and playful habits, has always been a favorite of man and a major attraction at zoos and marine parks. Because they live in water, dolphins and porpoises are often thought of as fish. In fact they are mammals and must, unlike fish, come up to the surface to breathe.

Bottle-nosed and other dolphins, along with porpoises and whales, all belong to a group of mammals called cetaceans (si-TAE-shuns). There

are two types of cetaceans, the Odontoceti (oh-dont-o-KET-ee), or toothed whales, and the Mysticeti (mist-uh-KET-ee), or baleen whales.

Dolphins and porpoises belong to the toothed whales, which use their teeth to seize their prey. Baleen whales, on the other hand, have no teeth. Instead they have comblike whalebone (or baleen) plates that hang from the roofs of their mouths and act as filters to strain out their food (small crustaceans, fish, and squid) from the seawater.

CLASSIFICATION

Dolphins and porpoises belong to the cetacean order. There are two types of cetaceans: Toothed whales belong to one suborder and baleen whales to the other. Toothed whales are divided into eight families, among them three families of dolphins and one of porpoises. These are further subdivided into 37 species.

ORDER
Cetacea
(whales)

SUBORDER
Odontoceti
(toothed whales)

SUPERFAMILY
Delphinoidea
(dolphins)

OCEANIC DOLPHIN FAMILY
Delphinidae

COASTAL DOLPHIN FAMILY
Stenidae

RIVER DOLPHIN FAMILY
Platanistidae

PORPOISE FAMILY
Phocoenidae

627

S. T. Westmorland/ZEFA-Allstock

Deep-swimming dolphins such as this dusky dolphin come up to the surface at intervals to breathe.

In general, the main difference between whales, dolphins, and porpoises is size: Whales are usually bigger than dolphins, which are usually bigger than porpoises. There are exceptions to this rule, however: The black dolphin, for example, is smaller than most porpoises.

There are one family of porpoises and three of dolphins: river, coastal, and oceanic. The dolphins have been divided up largely on the basis of habitat, but, again, there are many exceptions.

Dolphins, porpoises, and whales all seem to have descended from a group of land-living carnivores

THE FIRST DOLPHIN ANCESTORS LIVED ON LAND. AS THEY TOOK TO WATER, THEIR BODIES GRADUALLY CHANGED TO COPE WITH THEIR NEW ENVIRONMENT

called *mesonychids* (meez-ON-ik-ids), which lived between 60 and 35 million years ago. Some of these mammals took to the sea and their bodies changed to adapt to their new environment. (Other mesonychids stayed on land and eventually developed into grazing animals, such as the horse.)

The oldest recognizable cetacean was *Pakicetus* (pak-ee-KET-us). This creature, which looked similar to a large otter, lived about 50 million years ago and had a few adaptations to a marine existence, such as short, paddle-shaped limbs, but probably spent at least some of its time on land.

By 30 million years ago these early ancestors had

Kevin Schafer/NHPA

evolved to the point that they looked much more similar to today's cetaceans. *Eurhinodelphis* (you-rine-o-DEL-fis), for example, was a primitive porpoise with an elongated snout.

QUICK CHANGE

Although there were many advantages to living in the sea, such as a large food supply and plenty of space, the bodies of early cetaceans had to adapt to the aquatic environment before they could make maximum use of it. These changes took place

Bottle-nosed dolphins often swim in schools. Sometimes they swim just below the surface, with only the tops of their heads and their fins showing. They can then breathe through their exposed blowholes.

628

DOLPHIN OR WHALE?

François Gohier/Ardea

Despite their many similarities to dolphins, because of their size killer whales are classed as whales. As they have no beaks and fewer teeth than other whales, they, together with the pilot whales, have been put into a separate family—the Globicephalidae (globe-ee-kef-AL-id-ie).

Despite its name, the killer whale will not attack a human in the wild, though at least one dolphinarium trainer has been killed. Although some eat other sea mammals, killer whales feed mainly on fish and squid.

remarkably quickly in evolutionary terms.

Forelimbs turned into flippers and hind limbs—no longer needed—disappeared. The skeleton grew longer to support the two flukes that make up the tail. As the tail is moved up and down, the creature is propelled along.

The dolphin's body was then much more streamlined, which made it easier to travel quickly through water. Its skin also altered so that it could ripple with the water flow. This kept the animal from being slowed down too much by the turbulence of the water around it.

UNDER PRESSURE

To prevent its rib cage from getting crushed by the weight of water as the dolphin dives, some of its ribs float and others are jointed so that they can collapse under pressure.

Water pressure can cause other problems, too. In humans a sudden rise from the depths of the sea can cause a painful and sometimes lethal condition called the bends, the result of nitrogen bubbles forming in the tissues. Cetaceans do not suffer from the bends because, unlike human divers, they do not breathe air under pressure. Once underwater, the air in their

River dolphins such as the Yangtze (right) *are practically blind. Good eyesight would be useless, since they live in muddy water, and over millions of years the ability to see clearly has been lost.*

Nick Gordon/Survival Anglia

lungs is compressed, which means that no dangerous nitrogen can dissolve into the blood.

Cetaceans have separate nose and throat passages, and this prevents them from taking water into their lungs and drowning as they eat. They have no vocal cords, but nevertheless they do communicate with clicks and squeaks.

BREATHING IN

Air is breathed in through a single nostril or blowhole on top of the head, which is kept closed by a muscular flap that shuts automatically.

One of the most important adaptations to life in the sea is blubber. For deep-diving mammals it is a better insulator than fur, and it also acts as a food reserve. Blubber contains lots of blood vessels and, when these are open, heat can move more quickly to the surface of the skin and out of the

---

TO ADAPT TO THEIR WATERY HABITAT, DOLPHINS DEVELOPED FLIPPERS AND A TAIL, A BLOWHOLE, AND BLUBBER

---

body. When they are closed they stop the heat from escaping, and the animal is kept warm.

These numerous blood vessels have other purposes, too. They transport the oxygen taken in when the animal breathes. This is stored in the dolphin's blood and muscle and, when the dolphin dives, its heart rate slows down and the oxygen-rich blood is concentrated in the brain. ∎

THE DOLPHIN'S FAMILY TREE

It is impossible at present to show exactly how closely the various cetacean families are related to each other, because the truth is that we just do not know.

In fact, there is still much disagreement about how many dolphin families there are; while some authorities separate coastal and oceanic dolphins as we have done, others group them together under the family Delphinidae. However, it is clear that there are two main kinds of whales: toothed whales, which include dolphins and porpoises, and baleen whales.

RIVER DOLPHINS
Platanistidae (plat-an-IST-id-ie)

These dolphins all share certain characteristics, such as having poor eyesight, small brains, and long, slender beaks. However, we aren't sure whether they are closely related or whether they simply **look like each other because they evolved in the same freshwater habitat. River dolphins are the most primitive of the dolphins, resembling their fossil ancestors to a greater extent than the others.** **THERE ARE FIVE SPECIES:** AMAZON DOLPHIN, OR BOUTU *(SHOWN ABOVE)* BEIJI FRANCISCANA GANGES SUSU INDUS SUSU

COASTAL DOLPHINS
Stenidae (STEN-id-ie)

Sometimes known as the rough-toothed dolphins, this family was established fairly recently (in 1960) to separate out the four species that look much like the oceanic dolphins, but which **have a less specialized hearing system in their skulls. Other zoologists have classified these four dolphins as a subfamily of the Delphinidae.** **THERE ARE FOUR SPECIES:** ATLANTIC HUMP-BACKED DOLPHIN INDO-PACIFIC HUMP-BACKED DOLPHIN *(SHOWN ABOVE)* ROUGH-TOOTH DOLPHIN TUCUXI

SPERM WHALES

Illustrations Elisabeth Smith

OCEANIC DOLPHINS
Delphinidae (del-FIN-id-ie)

These are the least specialized of the dolphins, and therefore the most numerous. They are all less than 13 feet (4 meters) long and often have elaborate patterns of spots or stripes.

THERE ARE 34 SPECIES THAT INCLUDE:
ATLANTIC WHITE-SIDED DOLPHIN
BLACK (OR CHILEAN) DOLPHIN
BOTTLE-NOSED DOLPHIN (*SHOWN ABOVE*)

BRIDLED DOLPHIN
COMMERSON'S DOLPHIN
COMMON DOLPHIN
DUSKY DOLPHIN
FRASER'S DOLPHIN
HEAVISIDE'S DOLPHIN
HECTOR'S DOLPHIN

HOURGLASS DOLPHIN
IRRAWADDY DOLPHIN
KILLER WHALE
MELON-HEADED WHALE
PACIFIC WHITE-SIDED DOLPHIN

PEALE'S DOLPHIN
PILOT WHALE
RISSO'S DOLPHIN
SPINNER DOLPHIN
SPOTTED DOLPHIN
STRIPED DOLPHIN
WHITE-BEAKED DOLPHIN

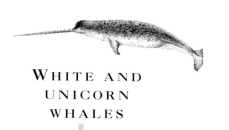

WHITE AND UNICORN WHALES

PORPOISES
Phocoenidae (fo-KON-id-ie)

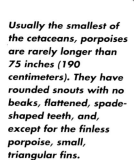

BEAKED WHALES

Usually the smallest of the cetaceans, porpoises are rarely longer than 75 inches (190 centimeters). They have rounded snouts with no beaks, flattened, spade-shaped teeth, and, except for the finless porpoise, small, triangular fins.

Porpoises have between 95 and 100 vertebrae, as compared to the 60 to 70 that the other dolphins have. Their skin is generally dark gray on their backs, shading to white on their bellies.

THERE ARE SIX SPECIES:
BURMEISTER'S PORPOISE
DALL'S PORPOISE
FINLESS PORPOISE
GULF OF CALIFORNIA PORPOISE (OR COCHITO) (*SHOWN ABOVE*)
HARBOR (OR COMMON) PORPOISE
SPECTACLED PORPOISE

TOOTHED WHALES

BALEEN WHALES

ALL WHALES
(CETACEA)

ANATOMY:
THE DOLPHIN

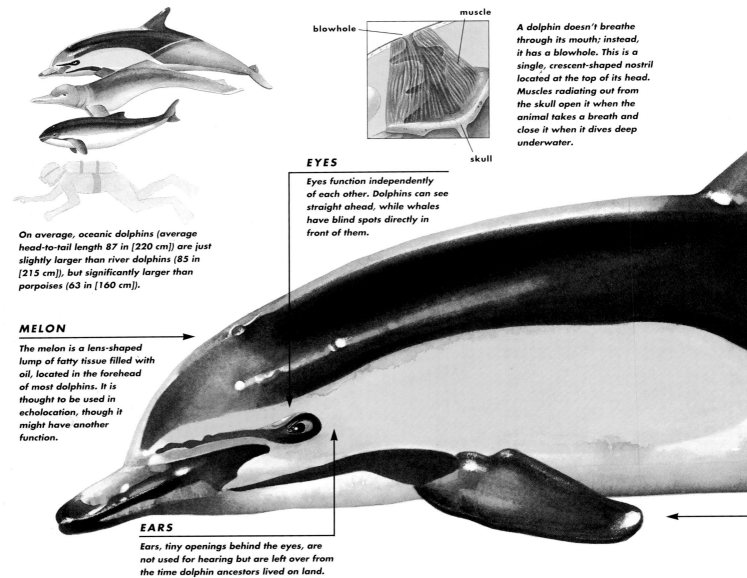

A dolphin doesn't breathe through its mouth; instead, it has a blowhole. This is a single, crescent-shaped nostril located at the top of its head. Muscles radiating out from the skull open it when the animal takes a breath and close it when it dives deep underwater.

muscle
blowhole
skull

On average, oceanic dolphins (average head-to-tail length 87 in [220 cm]) are just slightly larger than river dolphins (85 in [215 cm]), but significantly larger than porpoises (63 in [160 cm]).

EYES

Eyes function independently of each other. Dolphins can see straight ahead, while whales have blind spots directly in front of them.

MELON

The melon is a lens-shaped lump of fatty tissue filled with oil, located in the forehead of most dolphins. It is thought to be used in echolocation, though it might have another function.

EARS

Ears, tiny openings behind the eyes, are not used for hearing but are left over from the time dolphin ancestors lived on land.

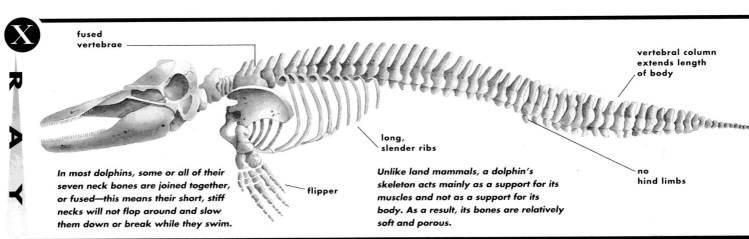

X RAY

fused vertebrae

vertebral column extends length of body

long, slender ribs

flipper

no hind limbs

In most dolphins, some or all of their seven neck bones are joined together, or fused—this means their short, stiff necks will not flop around and slow them down or break while they swim.

Unlike land mammals, a dolphin's skeleton acts mainly as a support for its muscles and not as a support for its body. As a result, its bones are relatively soft and porous.

A dolphin's skin, unlike that of most land mammals, is very smooth and more or less hairless: hair would only slow it down while it swims. Instead, the animal is kept warm by a thick layer of fat, called blubber, underneath the skin. Skin and blubber are attached to each other by small projections, and this allows the skin to ripple as the animal swims, thus reducing friction caused by turbulence.

blubber

projections

blood vessel

FINS

Fins are made of firm fatty tissue. They are used for stabilization; some cetaceans, such as the finless porpoise, have no fins.

STREAMLINED SHAPE

A streamlined, torpedo-shaped body enables the dolphin to move quickly and easily through the water.

FLIPPERS

Flippers are paddle-shaped and used for steering. The flipper's skeletal structure with its five finger bones is similar to that of a shortened human arm.

FLUKES

Flukes are the two lobes of the powerful horizontal tail that propel the animal through the water. Made of a tough, fibrous material, they are broad and flat.

FACT FILE:
THE COMMON DOLPHIN

CLASSIFICATION

GENUS: *Delphinus*

SPECIES: *delphis*

SIZE

HEAD–TAIL LENGTH/MALE: 87 IN (220 CM)

HEAD–TAIL LENGTH/FEMALE: 83 IN (210 CM)

WEIGHT/MALE: 190 LB (85 KG)

WEIGHT/FEMALE: 165 LB (75 KG)

HEAD–TAIL LENGTH AT BIRTH: 31 IN (80 CM)

COLORATION

VARIES GEOGRAPHICALLY: DARK BROWN OR BLACK ABOVE AND AROUND EYES, CREAM TO WHITE BELOW, WITH ELABORATE FIGURE-EIGHT PATTERN ON SIDES IN BUFF OR YELLOW AND LIGHT GRAY. SOME INDIVIDUALS HAVE WAVY GRAY LINES ON BELLY

FLIPPERS BLACK, LIGHT GRAY, OR WHITE

CALVES HAVE MORE MUTED COLOR PATTERNS

FEATURES

SLEEK, STREAMLINED BODY

TALL, SLENDER, POINTED FIN IN MIDDLE OF BACK; USUALLY CURVES BACKWARD

LONG, NARROW BEAK

BOUTU

blowhole

110 teeth

The skulls of dolphins and porpoises are asymmetrical, with the blowhole located at the top and slightly to the left. The harbor porpoise has relatively few teeth, while the common dolphin has about 200.

HARBOR PORPOISE

92 teeth

200 teeth

COMMON DOLPHIN

One difference between dolphins and porpoises lies in the shape of their teeth: Dolphins (left) have sharp pointed teeth, while those of porpoises (right) are flattened into a spade or chisel shape at the tips.

MAGICAL MARINERS

DOLPHINS AND PORPOISES HAVE CAST THEIR SPELL ON GENERATIONS OF OBSERVERS AND ARE INVARIABLY REFERRED TO AS "HIGHLY INTELLIGENT"— BUT WHAT IS THE TRUE NATURE OF THEIR MENTAL ABILITY?

From the time of the ancient Greeks, humankind has woven numerous tales celebrating the dolphin's friendliness. For centuries these were considered myths and nothing more. But in recent years there have been so many reports of dolphins coming to the assistance of people in trouble that it seems they may well have been true after all.

These include stories like the one from Mozambique in which a woman was rescued from sharks by a group of dolphins; or those from the wartime Pacific, which recount how American airmen, forced to bail out of their airplanes, were pushed ashore in their dinghies by dolphins.

ATTENTION-SEEKERS

Highly social and intelligent mammals, dolphins seem to genuinely enjoy the company of humans. In particular, they seek the attention of children, perhaps because children are smaller and gentler than adults. One bottle-nosed dolphin, which came to be known as Beaky, would often approach

---

"FRIENDLIES," DOLPHINS THAT ENJOY HUMAN COMPANY, RETURN TO THE SAME SPOT AGAIN AND AGAIN IN ORDER TO MAKE CONTACT WITH PEOPLE

---

swimmers around the Isle of Man and England's southwest coast during the 1970s, proving quite a tourist attraction. More recently, in Dingle on the southwest coast of Ireland, another bottle-nosed dolphin named Fungie has become a cult figure.

Dolphins appear to work their magic on people in other ways, too. Some claim that swimming with dolphins in the wild has helped them recover from mental illness. No one seems to know whether this is because the simple tactile pleasure of the

experience is so uplifting or whether the ultrasonic noises dolphins produce have a healing effect on the human mind.

RIDING THE WAVES

Dolphins also like to accompany seafaring vessels. Riding a ship's bow wave is a favorite dolphin occupation. They are able to get an (almost) free ride by swimming with the pressure wave that the vessel produces, though many experts believe dolphins also do it purely for fun. One particular dolphin, which came to be known as Pelorus Jack, began to accompany vessels in this manner across the Pelorus Sound in New Zealand in 1888 and continued to do so for twenty-four years.

Sometimes fishermen make use of dolphins to help them take a catch. The inhabitants of a village in the West African country of Mauritania

Paul Humann/Jeff Rotman Photography

Bottle-nosed dolphins (right) *ride a wave, while these spotted dolphins* (above) *prefer a more leisurely pace.*

Dolphins are among the most approachable of animals and present few problems to those who study them.

cooperate with dolphins when they camp out and wait for great schools of mullet to enter the Bay d'Argun.

As soon as the fish appear, the fishermen place their nets in the water and, when the fish jump and splash, the men hit the water with sticks to imitate the sound. Dolphins soon appear, drawn by the noise of splashing, and in doing so drive the fish into the villagers' nets.

The dolphins prosper from this arrangement in two ways: First, they can eat the escaping mullet; second, because of their importance to the catch, the villagers will never kill a dolphin deliberately. Only if one is washed up or stranded accidentally will they use it for oil or food.

MEASURE OF INTELLIGENCE

The apparent selflessness of some dolphin behavior can resemble that of human beings at their best. Because of this, some people have wondered if there are also similarities between the intellectual capabilities of dolphins and humans.

This avenue of thought seems to lead to a dead end. What appear to be "skills" to human observers are often just adaptations to the dolphin's environment. It is very difficult to measure dolphin intelligence, or that of any other animal for that matter, on a human-based scale when the world we inhabit is so very different from theirs.

When dolphin   first kept in captivity, it was hoped that humans might one day communicate with them. The dream remains an elusive one. ■

635

HABITATS

Hans Reinhard/Bruce Coleman Ltd.

Dolphins and porpoises inhabit every ocean except the coldest waters of the Arctic and Antarctic, though most species prefer temperate or tropical seas, where there is plenty of food all year round.

Some species, like hump-backed dolphins, prefer to live near to the shore, though they do venture farther out into the ocean to hunt. Others—such as the spinner and bridled dolphins—are pelagic species, which means they inhabit the open seas.

BECAUSE MANY DOLPHIN SPECIES TRAVEL A GREAT DEAL, THEY CAN BECOME COMMON IN AN AREA ONE YEAR AND THEN DISAPPEAR THE NEXT

Because dolphins and porpoises spend most of their lives beneath the surface of the water, it is difficult to study every species in detail. Some, like the very rare Gulf of California porpoise (or cochito), are studied closely only when they are washed up on the shore or caught by fishermen.

ON THE SURFACE

Dolphins and porpoises live at the top of the food chain. This food chain originates in the sun-dappled waters at the surface, home to the tiny plants, or phytoplankton, with which the chain begins. These plants get their energy needs from the sunlight through a process called photosynthesis and are found in the top 320 feet (100 meters) of the ocean. They are a concentrated source of nutrients and make up what are aptly named the "pastures of the sea."

Bottle-nosed dolphins are primarily a coastal species, although sightings are common in the open oceans.

The strange, solitary Amazon dolphin, or boutu, navigates the slow-moving, silt-laden river basins that pass through the forests of South America.

DISTRIBUTION

The bottle-nosed dolphin is found in all the warm and temperate waters of the world. Though the harbor porpoise has a more restricted distribution, it too is found in both the Pacific and Atlantic Oceans. The Indo-Pacific hump-backed dolphin inhabits the coastal waters, estuaries, and swamps of the Indian and Pacific Oceans, while the highly specialized boutu navigates the river systems of South America from the Atlantic to the Andes.

KEY

BOTTLE-NOSED DOLPHIN

HARBOR PORPOISE

INDO-PACIFIC HUMP-BACKED DOLPHIN

AMAZON RIVER DOLPHIN (BOUTU)

Tropic of Ca.

EQUATOR

Tropic of Ca.

Andrea Florence/Ardea

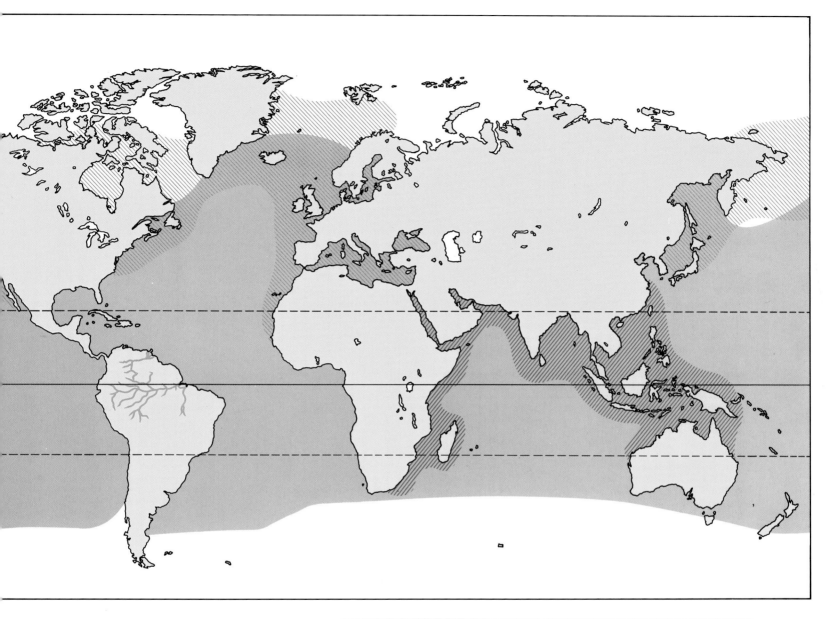

Tiny animals called zooplankton graze like cattle on the phytoplankton. These include the larvae of crustaceans, jellyfish, and bottom-living fish that start their life at the surface. They are eaten in turn by fish such as herring, which swim with their mouths open in order to gorge themselves on the plankton, and other species such as cod, mackerel, and anchovies, which form the dolphin's staple diet.

SEA OF PLENTY

Dolphins and porpoises are opportunists and often head for those areas affected by ocean currents such as the Humboldt Current. This flows off the west coast of South America and brings nutrient-rich cooler waters to the surface, which then sustain the food chain and provide ample feeding opportunities for the fish that prefer to live in warm

KEY FACTS

● The color and pattern of a dolphin's skin is a good guide to the kind of habitat that species prefers. Those that have dark skin prefer deeper waters, while those with black-and-white coloring blend well with the sun-dappled waters closer to the surface.

● No stranger to shallow coastal waters, the Indo-Pacific hump-backed dolphin uses its remarkably agile body to cross the mud banks that sometimes stand in the way of its journeys.

● Although harbor porpoises are most often found along the coasts and estuaries of the Northern Hemisphere, they occasionally make their way along major rivers. One once traveled over 200 miles (320 km) up Holland's Maas River.

waters. Dolphins and porpoises then proceed to feast on these incoming schools of fish.

Coastal waters also prove a happy hunting ground for dolphins. There the sea is enriched by sediments from the rivers that flow into it. In some parts of the world, especially northern Japan, West Africa, and Peru, the deposits from the ocean bed are moved by currents to the coast, and as a result they number among the world's finest fisheries.

COASTAL COMPANIONS

Along the coast, dolphins share their habitat with sponges, jellyfish, corals, and mollusks. There are also sea snakes, turtles, and many different seabirds, as well as other mammals like seals and otters.

Farther out to sea lie squid and octopus. The giant squid—which grows up to 65 feet (20 meters) long—is a ferocious creature when attacked. Even huge sperm whales have been found with scars on their skin made by the squid's tentacles.

A few dolphins live in a habitat very different from the open seas, such as the boutus of South

Bob Cranston/Jeff Rotman Photography

FOCUS ON
THE TROPICAL ATLANTIC

Bounded by Central and South America on the west and by West Africa on its eastern shores, the tropical Atlantic is a vast expanse of ocean that lies between the tropic of Cancer to the north and the tropic of Capricorn to the south.

The surface temperature of the tropical Atlantic is almost constant and is largely unaffected by any major currents. The surface waters, where most dolphins live, are uniformly warm.

Dolphins and porpoises thrive on the wide variety of fish that live there, such as tuna, hake, and herring. Other prey, which include octopuses, clams, lobsters, and crayfish, inhabit the coastal waters.

Apart from the dolphin fishing industry of the Azores and drift nets that may accidentally trap dolphins and porpoises, the greatest threats to dolphins in these waters are presented by predators like sharks and, in particular, the killer whale, ironically a close relation of dolphins and porpoises.

Two species particularly associated with this area are the spotted dolphin and the Atlantic hump-backed dolphin, but the tropical Atlantic is home to more than a dozen other species.

THE OCEAN LAYERS

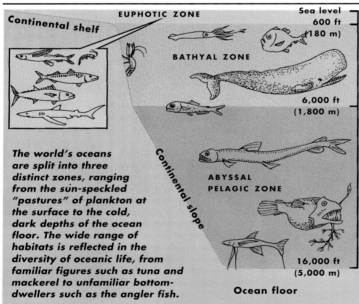

Douglas Ingram

The world's oceans are split into three distinct zones, ranging from the sun-speckled "pastures" of plankton at the surface to the cold, dark depths of the ocean floor. The wide range of habitats is reflected in the diversity of oceanic life, from familiar figures such as tuna and mackerel to unfamiliar bottom-dwellers such as the angler fish.

Continental shelf — EUPHOTIC ZONE — Sea level / 600 ft (180 m)
BATHYAL ZONE — 6,000 ft (1,800 m)
Continental slope
ABYSSAL PELAGIC ZONE — 16,000 ft (5,000 m)
Ocean floor

America. Good eyesight is of little use in the river's murky waters, and these dolphins rely on their echolocation system (see page 641) to catch the fish and crustaceans that make up their diet.

The dry season, when river levels are low, presents special problems for the boutus—particularly the inexperienced young—because they can become trapped in stagnant ponds. However, as long as the ponds do not dry up completely, the dolphins usually survive. ■

NEIGHBORS

These animals coexist with dolphins and porpoises and reflect the extraordinary variety of life found in the tropical Atlantic: from slow-moving, passive reptiles to swift, vigorous hunters.

MANTA RAY

The manta is famed for its jumping ability—and the reverberating crash it makes when it falls back into the sea.

BARRACUDA

Known as "the tiger of the sea," this fast and fierce hunter changes color to blend in with its surroundings.

Illustrations Lindsay Seers

ENEMIES

SEASONAL CHANGE IN THE TROPICS

The area of the tropical Atlantic is flexibly defined. When temperatures are at their warmest in the north (in August), the area defined as "tropical" reaches its northern limit. It reaches its southern limit in February, the south's warmest month.

■ AUGUST ▨ FEBRUARY

KILLER WHALE
Attacking in pods of five or six, killer whales will sometimes force other dolphins to stay underwater until they drown.

EXTREMELY DANGEROUS

GREAT WHITE SHARK
This giant of the tropical seas will attack anything that moves, though dolphins rarely number among its victims.

MODERATELY DANGEROUS

TIGER SHARK
Dolphins usually outwit sharks, but this fearsome opportunist poses a threat to old or sick creatures.

MODERATELY DANGEROUS

MORAY EEL	SAILFISH	PORTUGESE MAN-OF-WAR	BLUEFIN TUNA	GREEN TURTLE

The eel's snakelike body is perfectly suited to the nooks and crannies of tropical reefs where it searches for its prey.

Capable of speeds reaching 70 mph (110 km/h), this superbly streamlined fish is a game angler's favorite.

This dangerous jellyfish stings indiscriminately, secreting poison powerful enough to do serious harm to humans.

Closely related to mackerel, this tuna ranks among the largest of fish, reaching up to 12 ft (3.5 m) in length.

This huge, edible reptile lays hundreds of eggs on the seashore, then abandons its nest and returns to the ocean.

FOOD AND FEEDING

Dolphins and porpoises are primarily piscivores—fish-eaters—though most species will feed on squid and shrimp when the opportunity arises.

Dolphins and porpoises each have characteristic arrangements of teeth that reflect differences in their diets. Dolphins usually have long beaks containing a large number of very small, uniformly shaped teeth. Since they swallow food whole, without chewing it, the only function of their teeth is to seize their lively, slippery prey.

Those species of dolphins that eat squid, such as Risso's dolphin, have just a few teeth in their lower jaw and none at all in the upper, an adaptation that makes their hard-to-manage prey easier to suck in and swallow.

Porpoises have more specialized, chisel-like teeth, which act like shears and are more efficient at dealing with their prey of larger, smoother fish. Once caught, food is gulped down and goes directly into the animal's stomach, where it is slowly digested in a series of chambers.

Dazed and confused

Both dolphins and porpoises find their prey using a sophisticated system of echolocation (see box), similar to a submarine's sonar. It is possible that they also use pulses of sound to stun their prey. A high-frequency wave can kill small fish like anchovies, though more often it spreads confusion, enabling the dolphins to make an easy catch.

Different species of dolphins vary in their styles of hunting. Dusky dolphins, which are widespread along coastal areas of the southern hemisphere, hunt by day and stay near the shore at night. Whole schools of them may number as many as 400 individuals, but they divide up into small groups of about 30 for the hunt.

These dolphins spread out in a line and search the waters for schools of fish, even jumping out to

Lindsay Seers

SOUNDING OUT

The dolphin sends out a series of clicking noises, then times the delay as the echo bounces back. In this case a long delay means the dolphin's prey is still some distance away.

HOMING IN

With every move closer to the intended victim, the delay between echoes gets shorter. As the dolphin picks up more sound waves per second, the echoes get higher in pitch. It will soon be time to strike.

PREY

Dolphins and porpoises are opportunistic feeders. Most prefer relatively small fish, while a small number are squid specialists. Dolphins in coastal waters will take advantage of such creatures as octopuses and crustaceans.

MACKEREL	SQUID	FLYING FISH	ANCHOVY
			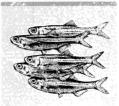

Illustrations Ruth Grewcock

look for hovering seabirds, which might tell them where their prey is to be found. When they find a school, they leap out of the water and splash down to frighten the fish, forcing them to the surface. They then take turns swimming through the seething mass of fish until they have had their fill.

Group hunting can be a spectacular sight. Sometimes a group of dolphins will drive a school of fish onto the shore, and an individual might even follow them right onto the sand, struggling back to the sea with a fish in its mouth.

Bottle-nosed dolphins often encircle a school of fish, and then each in turn will swim to the center to eat. Unfortunately for the dolphins, killer whales have been known to employ the same tactics on them, squeezing dolphins into a tight circle before rushing in on them in a deadly attack.

NEIGHBORHOOD WATCH

Some species of dolphins cooperate with other species in their search for prey. While the spotted dolphin is alert and on the lookout for predators during the day, a night-hunting species like the spinner dolphin may rest nearby, relying on its spotted dolphin neighbors to warn it of danger. The nocturnal spinner dolphins return the favor during the night.

Most species of dolphins

THE DOLPHIN'S SONAR

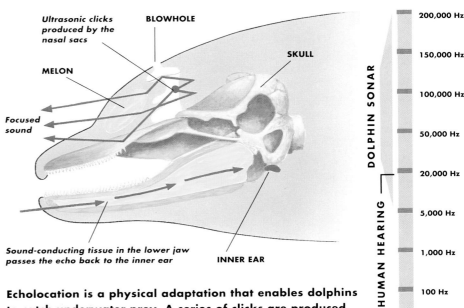

Ultrasonic clicks produced by the nasal sacs

BLOWHOLE

SKULL

MELON

Focused sound

Sound-conducting tissue in the lower jaw passes the echo back to the inner ear

INNER EAR

DOLPHIN SONAR

HUMAN HEARING

200,000 Hz
150,000 Hz
100,000 Hz
50,000 Hz
20,000 Hz
5,000 Hz
1,000 Hz
100 Hz
20 Hz
1 Hz

Echolocation is a physical adaptation that enables dolphins to catch underwater prey. A series of clicks are produced by air vibrating in the dolphin's nasal sacs. These are located behind the melon, a lump of fatty tissue in front of the skull, which focuses a beam of sound varying from between 20 and 800 vibrations per second. When the sound waves hit an object, they are reflected back to the dolphin's brain. From the returning echoes the dolphin can figure out the position of its intended victim.

Douglas Ingram

and porpoises need to eat at least 20 pounds (9 kilograms) of fish every day, so they need to live near a good supply of food. Cooler waters are often the richest sources of food, so some species live in such areas or move there seasonally. Some migrate annually, like the striped dolphin, which goes south to the Sagami Bay fisheries off the east coast of Japan's Izu Peninsula every autumn. ■

"X-RAY VISION"

The dolphin receives a transparent image of a fish. This is because the sound waves emitted by the dolphin pass right through the fish's tissue and are reflected by its bones and swim bladder.

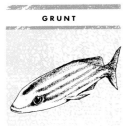

GRUNT

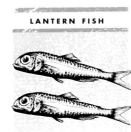

LANTERN FISH

OCTOPUS

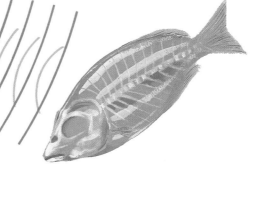

SOCIAL STRUCTURE

With the exception of river dolphins, which generally lead rather solitary lives, dolphins and porpoises live in social groups called schools or pods. These may be small, consisting of only two individuals, or vast, with thousands of dolphins swimming together in the oceans and seas. Most schools number between 20 and 100; schools of a thousand or more are divided up into smaller groups that interrelate with each other.

FAMILY TIES

Dolphins are notoriously difficult to observe in the wild. However, one long-term and detailed study has been conducted on bottle-nosed dolphins in Sarasota Bay, Florida. Here, the dolphins divide up into distinct groups within a school.

Mothers with calves swim near the center of a school, where they are protected from predators. Young adult males form their own groups and are

---

DOLPHINS COMMUNICATE CONSTANTLY WITH OTHER MEMBERS OF THE SAME SCHOOL AND FORM STRONG BONDS WITH ONE ANOTHER

---

sometimes joined by juvenile females, who return to their mothers when they reach sexual maturity. Adult males may wander temporarily from the school, mating with females of other schools.

Schools of dolphins often swim in unison, leaping spectacularly out of the water at exactly the same moment. This enables them to breathe at the same time so that, when they dive, they are synchronized for hunting prey and rounding up fish. Like herds of deer, they have a group awareness that helps them find food and alerts them to approaching predators.

Although different species of dolphins swim together from time to time, there is usually very little social interaction between them. Bottle-nosed dolphins are sometimes seen swimming with herds of pilot whales, but fishermen have also seen melon-headed whales and pilot whales attacking other dolphins during fishing activities.

TAKING TURNS

A social hierarchy in which individuals know their places often exists within a group of dolphins. Fishermen in Australia found that male bottle-nosed dolphins will place themselves in the best position to get fish from the shrimp nets, while females and juveniles have to make do with what is left.

A hierarchy may also exist between different species. One ship's crew noticed that, when riding the bow wave of their ship, common dolphins dropped back to allow white-sided dolphins to take

INSIGHT

A FRIEND IN NEED

Dolphins often form close ties with other members of the same school. They will go to the aid of a dolphin in distress and protect it from danger or help it if it is wounded and unable to swim.

In an attempt to save an injured dolphin, school members will hold the victim up as it swims and help it take in air. Using their own bodies as support, they will take the wounded animal to the surface of the water every so often so that it can breathe.

Robert Visser/Greenpeace

Illustrations David Thompson/Wildlife Art Agency

When they swim together, dolphins often surface to breathe and dive at exactly the same moment.

the best position; then they, in turn, were displaced by bottle-nosed dolphins.

Dolphins in the same school communicate with each other using a kind of basic language. They make a series of groans, clicks, and whistles to convey information to other dolphins, like "help!" or "keep together." When they pick up a distress signal, dolphins will go to the aid of a dolphin in danger or they will rally together to fend off predators. Each individual dolphin has its own "signature tune," or distinctive whistle, by which it is identified by others in the pod.

Studies of captive dolphins have shown that loud noises accompanied by jaw clapping and tail slapping mean that the animal is angry; louder and faster noises indicate that it is excited or upset. The soft chirping noises that a dolphin makes when it is being stroked mean it is happy. ■

COOPERATIVE HUNTING IN BOTTLE-NOSED DOLPHINS

When a large group of dolphins finds a school of fish, they work together to round up their prey. The dolphins swim around the outside of the school in tighter and tighter circles, herding the fish into a smaller area. Then they move in and start to feed, catching the fish in their teeth.

KEY FACTS

● Most dolphins and porpoises live in groups called schools or pods. A school usually contains between 20 and 100 dolphins.

● Adult males and females may form separate groups within a school but still interact with each other. A social hierarchy in which males are dominant often exists within a school.

● River dolphins are usually solitary animals, but they are sometimes seen swimming in small groups of three or four.

REPRODUCTION

Dolphins mate seasonally, from spring to autumn. When the season arrives, a male dolphin may discourage rivals by loudly smacking its jaws. If another male comes too close, it will bite him or lash out with its powerful tail.

CLOSE TIES

Mating among most species of dolphins seems promiscuous—both males and females mate with as many other individuals as possible. Pair bonding is apparently not important to successful reproduction. Mating usually takes place belly to belly.

Halfway through pregnancy, which lasts between ten and twelve months, the prospective mother moves to the edge of the group and chooses another female to act as midwife. Sometimes this may be an older daughter of her own. Until the calf

Dolphins mating

is due, the midwife spends most of her time with the expectant mother.

Several weeks before the calf is born, the expectant mother begins to arch and stretch her body for a short time each day, as if she were exercising in preparation for the rigors of birth.

Baby dolphins are born tail first, a necessity because the birth can take two hours, and if the blowhole were to emerge too soon, the baby would drown.

THE NEW ARRIVAL

The calf is born with the help of the midwife, who may support the mother with her own body. Once the umbilical cord is bitten through, the mother guides the newborn up to the surface for its first breath of air.

Young dolphins and porpoises are born with their eyes open and can swim soon after birth. In some species the body is covered with a minute stubble, which soon disappears; it is a reminder that dolphins once had fur, like most other mammals. The fins and flukes are folded and soft, but within an hour they harden into position. Calves have large bodies in proportion to their mothers, which may be an adaptation to help them keep warm. (The bigger an animal is, the less body heat it loses to the water.) A newborn bottle-nosed dolphin, for instance, weighing 55 pounds (25 kilograms), is about a sixth of the size of its mother, which weighs about 330

2. *The newborn calf is not yet buoyant because it has no air in its lungs. The exhausted mother has to carry the calf to the surface of the water, supporting it across her own body.*

A HELPING HAND

Several months before she gives birth, a female dolphin chooses another experienced female to act as a midwife. The two females move away to the edge of the group, and from then on the midwife stays with the pregnant female to look after her until the baby is born. As she will have had at least one calf of her own, the midwife is the mother's help and support when the baby arrives. A strong bond often develops between the two females during this time.

Illustrations David Thompson/Wildlife Art Agency

3. *Once its body has broken through the surface of the water, the calf's blowhole immediately opens and it takes its first breath of air.*

in SIGHT

Denise Herzing/Ardea

LACTATION

1. *During the birth (left), the midwife encourages the mother. When the calf is finally born (above), the mother bites through the umbilical cord and acts quickly to take the calf to the surface.*

pounds (150 kilograms).

The female dolphin suckles her calf for 12 to 18 months, although after four months the baby begins to eat fish. For the first few weeks it remains close to its mother's side, staying near her body where the water flow carries it along as she swims. As it grows older it becomes more adventurous, swimming farther away to explore its surroundings.

Female dolphins bear calves every two or three years, usually having a total of eight in a lifetime. Usually dolphins have only one calf, but very rarely twins are born. In some species of porpoises, though, females have traces of several sets of nipples, which suggests that at some time in their ancient past it was normal for them to suckle a number of young. ■

Within 24 hours of birth the baby dolphin takes its first drink of milk. The mother's two teats are hidden in long slits near her tail, and because the shape of the baby's jaws makes it impossible for it to suck, she squirts milk into its mouth using her muscles. The calf takes hold of the teat with its tongue, forming a channel down which the milk flows into its throat. After feeding, the baby swims to the surface for air. At first it needs milk every 20 minutes. Because dolphin milk is very nutritious, rich in fat and protein, the baby doubles its birth weight in only two months.

A WATERY GRAVE

DOLPHINS HAVE INSPIRED AND ENTHRALLED PEOPLE FOR THOUSANDS OF YEARS, BUT TODAY DOLPHINS AND PORPOISES EVERYWHERE ARE SEVERELY UNDER THREAT. TWO SPECIES MAY EVEN BECOME EXTINCT BEFORE THE END OF THIS CENTURY

Reports of dolphins and porpoises dying at the hands of humans are on the increase. Drowning in fishnets is the most serious threat. Thousands are killed for their meat every year, and many suffer from a decreased supply of food through overfishing or pollution.

In Japan, where dolphin meat is a delicacy, at least 14,500 small cetaceans are killed a year to supply meat to local markets. Of those killed, about 10,000 are Dall's porpoises; others include striped, spotted, bottle-nosed and Pacific white-sided

---

ALL OVER THE WORLD DOLPHINS ARE BEING CAPTURED IN FISHNETS—BOTH ACCIDENTALLY AND DELIBERATELY— WHERE THEY FACE DEATH BY DROWNING

---

dolphins. Off the coasts of Peru, 10,000 dolphins are killed annually for food, particularly dusky dolphins, Burmeister's porpoises and bottle-nosed dolphins.

Dolphins and porpoises, are also hunted to a lesser extent in the South Pacific, Venezuela, Chile, and by the fishermen of France and Spain.

Each year, thousands of dolphins become tangled in fishnets. All around the world, fishermen are switching to using gill nets because they are cheap, easy to use, and an efficient way of catching fish when stocks are low.

THE DANGERS OF GILL NETS

When a fish swims into these square-meshed nets, it is caught behind the gills; hence the name. A gill net is invisible to a dolphin and, once it has become entangled, it cannot break free and eventually drowns. Gill nets are not selective and catch everything in their path. Scientists have estimated that several hundred thousand dolphins and porpoises die in this way every year.

Populations of the cochito have been so severely reduced by the use of gill nets set by Mexican fishermen that a recent survey yielded sightings of only thirty-one individuals.

Scientists have been experimenting with devices attached to the nets that would make them more visible to dolphins, but there has been little success.

TUNA FISHERIES

The greatest single cause of death for dolphins occurs in the waters of Central America, in an area known as the eastern tropical Pacific, where at least 100,000 dolphins were being killed every year by the yellowfin tuna industry. At least six million dolphins have died there in the past 30 years.

Yellowfin tuna swim beneath schools of some species of dolphins, and fishermen use the dolphins as visual markers to find the tuna. Speedboats and

Thousands of dolphins are hunted every year in countries such as Japan and Peru. The bodies are then butchered and sent to local meat markets.

This map shows the possible change in numbers of small cetaceans around Britain, based on reported sightings. Sightings from 1940 are from memory.

SIGHTINGS 1940s   SIGHTINGS 1980s

Numbers of dolphins and porpoises have fallen dramatically as a result of fishing activities, hunting, and marine pollution. Populations are most affected in

- the eastern tropical Pacific
- Japan, Peru, Venezuela, and Chile
- the northeast Atlantic, particularly the North Sea and the Irish Sea

The graph below shows estimated numbers (in thousands) of spotted and spinner dolphins in the eastern tropical Pacific from 1959 to 1986. (Note that this is not a linear scale.)

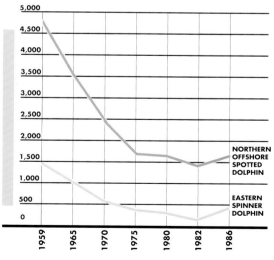

647

ENDANGERED ENVIRONMENT

sometimes explosives are used to herd the tuna—and the dolphins—into a bunch and a mile-long net (called a purse seine) is set around them. In this way, both tuna and dolphins are caught and, although attempts are made to release the dolphins, many drown. Some local populations, such as the eastern spinner dolphin, may have declined by as much as 80 percent as a result of this tuna fishery.

As a result of public pressure, most tuna fishermen have now stopped fishing in the eastern tropical Pacific and populations should recover. Tuna elsewhere is caught in other ways, either by purse seining on free-swimming schools of tuna, for example, or by pole and line fishing. Many tuna canners now advertise their tuna as "dolphin-friendly," though some have been caught cheating.

HUNDREDS OF THOUSANDS OF DOLPHINS HAVE BEEN KILLED IN THE EASTERN TROPICAL PACIFIC AS A BY-CATCH OF THE YELLOWFIN TUNA FISHERY

In other places, dolphins suffer because of overfishing: When this happens their food supply is significantly reduced. For example, harbor porpoises used to be a common sight in the southern North Sea and the English Channel, but, since the herring stock was drastically depleted in the 1950s as a result of reckless overfishing, these porpoises have become extremely rare in this area.

MARINE POLLUTION

Dolphins are also at risk from pollution and the destruction of their habitat. Toxic chemicals are produced as by-products of many industrial activities and are released into the environment.

One example of toxic chemicals is a group called organochlorines, which are carbon-based compounds such as PCBs, or polychlorinated biphenyls. These are produced during the chlorine-bleaching of paper pulp, the manufacture of pesticides, the incineration of garbage, and as a part of some electrical components. These chemicals are released into the sea and build up in the bodies of dolphins.

Many pollutants, including PCBs, are fat soluble and are stored in the blubber and other fat reserves of dolphins. When the dolphin uses these fat reserves as food, large amounts of poisonous chemicals are released into the blood.

In Britain, pollution is believed to be causing declines in harbor porpoises and bottle-nosed dolphins. Recently, mass die-offs of dolphins are thought to have been caused by pollutants lowering the animals' resistance to disease. In 1990 and 1991, striped dolphins in the Mediterranean were washed

Background William Curtsinger/ZEFA–Allstock

THE NORTH SEA: DOLPHINS AND POLLUTION

The dumping of toxic waste in the sea is a major threat to marine mammals, affecting their ability to reproduce and their immunity to disease. One heavily polluted area is the North Sea.

TOXIC WASTE

The rivers that flow into the North Sea contain chemical waste, or effluent, from several of the major industrialized cities of Europe. These rivers wash poisonous heavy metals—zinc, cadmium, copper, mercury, and lead—and organic compounds into the sea.

Organochlorines—a group of carbon-based toxic chemicals—accumulate in the blubber of dolphins and seals. This group of chemicals includes PCBs, or polychlorinated biphenyls, which are produced as a result of many industrial processes. Until production was banned in the 1970s, about 1.3 million tons of PCBs were manufactured worldwide. Thirty-one percent of

MANY DIFFERENT KINDS OF TOXIC CHEMICALS ARE BEING DUMPED DIRECTLY INTO THE NORTH SEA.

CONSERVATION MEASURES

● For years, environmental groups such as Greenpeace have been campaigning to stop toxic waste from being leaked into the seas.

● As a result, the 1990 North Sea Ministers Conference agreed to commit international resources to research on small cetaceans and to minimize the impact of human activities on marine wildlife. A survey of UK

this total—407,000 tons—has been released into the environment.

In 1987, the UK dumped over eleven million tons of waste directly into the sea, some of which was heavily polluted industrial waste, sewage sludge, or the residues from incinerators. This dumping has now been stopped, but the damage has already been done.

Around 50 percent of the pollutants that arrive in the North Sea are airborne. These are produced by the incineration of waste and industry emissions. For example, the incomplete combustion of organochlorines releases some of the most toxic chemicals known: dioxins. Tiny amounts can cause cancer and birth defects and affect the immune system.

For too long we have regarded the seas as dumping grounds for all kinds of waste. Now, at last, some action is being taken, but scientists fear that it might be too little and too late.

DOLPHINS IN DANGER

THE CHART BELOW SHOWS HOW THE INTERNATIONAL UNION FOR THE CONSERVATION OF NATURE (IUCN) CLASSIFIES DOLPHINS AND PORPOISES. ALTHOUGH IT IS SUSPECTED THAT MOST DOLPHIN SPECIES ARE UNDER THREAT, IT IS VERY DIFFICULT TO COUNT NUMBERS OF PRESENT POPULATIONS AND THE IUCN IS UNABLE TO CLASSIFY MOST OF THEM. SOME ANALYSIS HAS BEEN MADE: A SPECIES IS VULNERABLE IF NUMBERS HAVE FALLEN, AND A SPECIES IS ENDANGERED IF ESTIMATED NUMBERS OF 2,000 OR FEWER REMAIN:

AMAZON DOLPHIN (BOUTU)	VULNERABLE
GANGES DOLPHIN (SUSU)	VULNERABLE
INDUS DOLPHIN (SUSU)	ENDANGERED
YANGTZE DOLPHIN (BEIJI)	ENDANGERED
GULF OF CALIFORNIA PORPOISE (COCHITO)	ENDANGERED

ENDANGERED MEANS THAT THE ANIMAL IS IN DANGER OF EXTINCTION AND ITS SURVIVAL IS UNLIKELY UNLESS STEPS ARE TAKEN TO SAVE IT. VULNERABLE INDICATES THAT THE ANIMAL IS LIKELY TO MOVE INTO THE ENDANGERED CATEGORY IF THINGS CONTINUE AS THEY ARE.

Marty Snyderman/Planet Earth Pictures

Hoffman/Greenpeace

coastal waters and protected marine habitats was also proposed.

● By 1997 Sweden aims to have phased out three chlorinated solvents, and all uses of PVC are to be phased out in Germany. The Netherlands, Switzerland, Sweden, Austria, Denmark, and Germany have all voluntarily agreed to restrict the use of PVC in their packaging material.

up dead in large numbers. Four years before, large numbers of dead bottle-nosed dolphins were washed up along the east coast of the United States— estimated at a loss of at least half the local population.

TO SUIT MAN'S NEEDS

Some people perceive the capture of dolphins from the wild for show in zoos and wildlife parks as a threat to their survival. However, these few captive animals, many of which now breed in captivity, have inspired millions to speak out for dolphin protection. Modern zoos and aquaria employ scientific teams to address issues of health, comfort, and psychological well-being. Nowadays, the shows emphasize natural behaviors rather than simple animal tricks.

River dolphins are severely under threat as a result of man's activities. The proposed construction of hydroelectric dams on the Amazon River will destroy the habitat of the boutu, which, together with the cochito, is already considered one

NEW TUNA FISHING TECHNIQUES

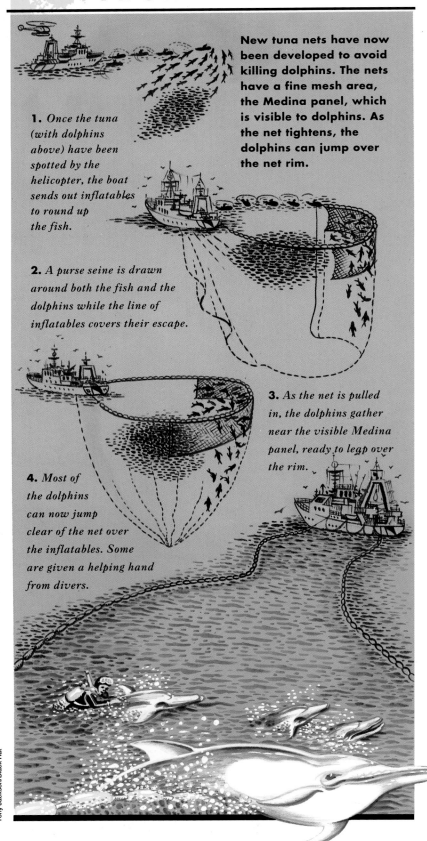

New tuna nets have now been developed to avoid killing dolphins. The nets have a fine mesh area, the Medina panel, which is visible to dolphins. As the net tightens, the dolphins can jump over the net rim.

1. *Once the tuna (with dolphins above) have been spotted by the helicopter, the boat sends out inflatables to round up the fish.*

2. *A purse seine is drawn around both the fish and the dolphins while the line of inflatables covers their escape.*

3. *As the net is pulled in, the dolphins gather near the visible Medina panel, ready to leap over the rim.*

4. *Most of the dolphins can now jump clear of the net over the inflatables. Some are given a helping hand from divers.*

Tony Jackson/Black Hat

Kenneth W. Fink/Ardea

Flashy tricks such as this are no longer in favor. Now, natural behaviors are emphasized.

of the most endangered of cetacean species. Only a few individuals remain. River dolphins are also threatened by boat traffic on rivers. The noise of the engines upsets their echolocation systems, and when they are disorientated, river dolphins cannot hunt for food. Sometimes these dolphins are seriously injured or killed by underwater propellers.

Dolphins and porpoises have little international protection. The Marine Mammal Protection Act, which came into force in 1972, gave strict protection to all marine mammals in U.S. waters, but the fishing industry there was so powerful that it was able to continue killing dolphins. Now, although some countries have enacted similar laws, dolphins have little protection worldwide. In December 1992

> THE USE OF HIGH-SEAS GILL NETS IS NOW ILLEGAL, BUT THE KILLING OF DOLPHINS AND PORPOISES MAY YET CONTINUE. MORE PROTECTION IS NEEDED

the United Nations Resolution banning high-seas gill nets came into effect, but it remains to be seen whether it will be effective in the long term or whether new ways will be found by the fisheries to continue this practice.

Although the outlook for dolphins and porpoises seems grim, many people are now aware of their plight and there is hope that steps will be taken to secure their survival. The threats to dolphin populations, however, are so varied, and frequently so complex, that there seems to be no simple solution. One thing is clear: Dolphins and porpoises need much more protection. ■

INTO THE FUTURE

The future for dolphins is uncertain, owing to the impact of a rapidly increasing human population on the marine environment. There are many toxic time bombs around the world: It has been suggested that if all the dioxins present in old electrical equipment were released into the seas, the extinction of all dolphins and porpoises would be inevitable.

PREDICTION

YANGTZE DOLPHIN (BEIJI)

Even though efforts are being made to save the beiji, such as setting up semicaptive preserves, by the next century this animal may be extinct in the wild.

With the benefit of modern technology, however, it is now possible for industry to use clean production techniques, where no waste is released and chemicals are reused within the system. For example, paper can be bleached using hydrogen peroxide rather than chlorine, thus avoiding the production of dioxins and environmental pollution. Changing to clean technologies often costs money, though, and may have to be stimulated by legislation or consumer demand for a "greener" product.

Except for the beiji, whose future may be possible only in seminatural reserves, captive breeding will not solve the problem of declining populations. It is extremely difficult to keep

PREDICTION

COCHITO

Extremely low numbers of the cochito survive. Mexico has just created a reserve to protect it, and if there is adequate enforcement, this species may yet be saved.

dolphins in captivity and very hard to persuade them to breed there.

The health of dolphins acts as a barometer to measure the health of the oceans. If we can secure the dolphin's future, the conservation of the many other plants and animals that share their watery home may follow. ∎

RIVER DOLPHINS

All five species of river dolphins are threatened by extinction. The construction of dams fragments the population, river pollution destroys their habitat, and collision with boats kills many animals. Their prospects for the future are poor, and, until recently, there has been little research to determine the best ways to protect them.

Scientists have met with the World Bank and other funding organizations with a view to ensuring that the needs of these dolphins are taken into consideration when future developments are planned. Research projects geared to their conservation needs are now starting up. For example, to protect the beiji, parts of the Yangtze River are being designated as preserves. At the same time, seminatural preserves are also being set up and research is being carried out to develop techniques for keeping the animals in captivity. In Peru, the density of river dolphins in various habitats is being studied to estimate how populations are faring in different areas.

PROTECTED AREAS

The cochito in the Gulf of California is at risk of extinction and needs help now. The only way to save it is for local conservationists to work with the fishermen to make sure that illegal gillnetting in the area is stopped entirely. Like most species of porpoises, cochitos are hard to study. Scientists, sometimes using acoustic techniques, can locate the most important habitats for this species and these areas could be better protected. The more we know about the animal's needs, the more we can help it survive.

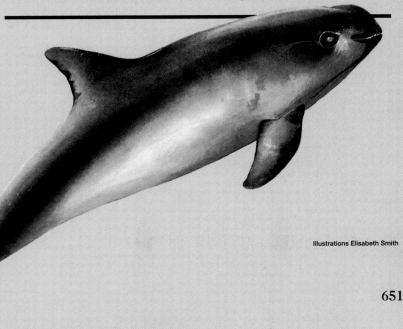

Illustrations Elisabeth Smith

ELEPHANTS

Jim Brandenburg/ZEFA–Minden

Elephants belong to a group of mammals called proboscideans, or "animals with trunks," and to the suborder Elephantoidea. The only surviving family of the Elephantoidea are the true elephants. This family is further broken down into the two remaining officially recognized elephant species, the African and the Asian.

ORDER

Proboscidea
(animals with trunks)

SUBORDER

Elephantoidea
(elephantlike forms)

FAMILY

Elephantidae
(elephants)

AFRICAN ELEPHANT GENUS

Loxodonta

SPECIES

africana

ASIAN ELEPHANT GENUS

Elephas

SPECIES

maximus

THE GENTLE GIANT

FEW ANIMALS CAPTURE THE IMAGINATION LIKE THE ELEPHANT, BUT TODAY'S SPECIES ARE MERELY THE FINAL CHAPTERS IN A REMARKABLE EVOLUTIONARY TALE THAT BEGAN FIFTY-FIVE MILLION YEARS AGO

The elephant's imposing stature and docile temperament combine to make it one of the best loved of animals. But, despite a continuing power to amaze and inspire, the gentle giants we see in zoological gardens are their species ambassadors, reminding humans that Africa without elephants is a real possibility unless we continue to care.

Elephants are megaherbivores, or large animals that eat plants on a massive scale. Everything about their lifestyle is dictated by their need for huge tracts of land capable of meeting their enormous daily food intake. This endless consumption of vegetation is made possible by the animal's enormous jaws and lozengelike teeth.

The elephant's most distinguishing feature is its strong but flexible trunk. Formed from the union of the nose and upper lip, the trunk is made up of thousands of tiny muscles, making it capable not only of incredible power but also the most precise

653

and delicate movements. It enables the elephant to take food from anywhere—from ground level up to the branches of trees taller than itself.

Today, there are two elephant species, the African elephant and the Asian elephant. It was thought that a third, smaller species existed in the swamps of central Africa—the pygmy elephant—but it is now believed to have been the observation of precocial tusk development in a few juvenile African elephants.

SIZE AND STATURE

The African elephant is the largest land animal alive, standing at 10 to 13 feet (3 to 4 meters) high and weighing around 13,200 pounds (6,000 kilograms). There are two subspecies, the forest elephant and the savanna elephant.

> ONE BULL, KILLED IN ANGOLA IN 1955, WEIGHED AN INCREDIBLE 22,000 POUNDS (ABOUT 10,000 KILOGRAMS) AND STOOD 13 FEET (4 METERS) HIGH

Throughout their lives, elephants keep growing, which means that the biggest elephants are usually the oldest. The biggest elephants of all are the African savanna bulls.

To support such bulk, the legs of the elephant are made up of pillars of thick bone supported by fatty tissue and broad feet that help spread the elephant's weight. Considering their size, elephants are remarkably light on their feet.

African elephants normally have long ivory tusks which, like the elephant itself, continue to grow

Frans Lanting/ZEFA-Minden

Adrian Warren/Ardea

A male Asian elephant, complete with tusks, in its forest habitat. Note the prominent domed head and the scattering of brown hair on its head and back.

THE BIG PYGMY

Harold N. Nestroy

The question of a third, smaller elephant species, *Loxodonta pumilio*, was first raised by German zoologist Theodore Noack in 1906. The so-called "pygmy" elephant, averaging about 6 feet (2 meters) in height, is said to inhabit the swamps of central Africa. Despite the fact that native peoples recognize a separate species, and that some Westerners claim to have observed such creatures, the scientific establishment remains doubtful about its existence.

throughout the creature's life and may weigh as much as 130 pounds (60 kilograms). They are, in fact, extended incisor teeth that first appear when the animal is about two years old.

The Asian elephant is smaller than the African, weighing up to about 11,000 pounds (5,000 kilograms) and reaching a height of 8 to 10 feet (2.4 to 3 meters). Its head features a prominent dome and its ears, compared with those of the African, are relatively small and more triangular in shape. While the African elephant has two fleshy, mobile protruberances, or "fingers," on its trunk, the Asian elephant has only one. These enable the elephant to manipulate objects with some dexterity, though the fact that the Asian elephant has only a single finger does not seem to be a significant handicap.

LAST IN A LONG LINE

African and Asian elephants are the only surviving members of an order of about 350 species of mammals called Proboscidae (pro-BOSS-kid-ie), or "animals with trunks." One of the most important of these, the hippopotamus-like moeritheres (mo-er-REE-theers), were ancestors to a range of sea-living mammals alive today, including sea cows, manatees, and dugongs.

Another line from the moeritheres led to the rodentlike rock hyrax, which still survives. Unlikely as it may seem for such a small creature, it is thought to be the elephant's closest living relative. Another strain led to the paleomastodons (pay-lee-o-MASS-to-dons), a family of huge, elephantlike animals. Following their decline, a five-million-year gap appears in the fossil record before the mastodons emerged.

AFRICAN DAWN

Once common throughout the world, mastodons looked a lot like modern elephants, but they had a real bottom jaw. One species of mastodon, the *gomphotherium* (gom-fo-THEER-ee-um) was an ancestor of *primelephas* (prime-EL-ee-fass). It was

> THE ASIAN AND AFRICAN ELEPHANTS
> REPRESENT THE CULMINATION OF AN
> AMAZING EVOLUTIONARY TALE—THEY
> ARE AMONG THE LAST MEGAHERBIVORES

from this direct line that the African elephant first appeared about five million years ago.

Once, up to ten million elephants could lay claim to being among the dominant species of Africa and Asia. Today, huge swaths of these two continents are under cultivation, zigzagged by roads and dotted with cities. But elephants, along with a handful of other megaherbivores such as hippos, giraffes, and rhinos, still survive as reminders of a time when the world was a very different place. ■

NCESTORS

PLATYBELODON (plat-ee-BEL-o-don)
A relatively small proboscidean, platybelodon is one of the most unusual ancestors of the modern elephant. It belonged to a group of animals called the *gomphotheres*, which lived about 20 million years ago. While its upper tusks were quite small, its lower tusks were flattened, giving them the appearance of a shovel. These are thought to have been used for uprooting vegetation from the marshes that were once common throughout Asia.

STEGODON (STEG-o-don)
An inhabitant of the forests of Asia some 2 million years ago, stegodon was another real giant among proboscideans. At 11.5 feet (3.5 meters) it was larger than the modern African elephant. Even more distinctive than its imposing stature were its formi-dable curving tusks, so large they almost touched the ground. Unfortunately for stegodon, it appears that its tusks grew so closely together that they left little room for the trunk.

MAMMUTHUS IMPERATOR (MAM-a-thuss im-PER-a-tor)
One of seven species of mammoths, this was the largest of the proboscideans and, interestingly, is more closely related to the modern Asian elephant than the Asian is to the modern African species. The "imperial mammoth" reached a height of 14 feet (4.3 meters) and lived throughout North America. Its incredible tusks must have struck fear into the hearts of early man, for whom it was an important source of food. Man's hunting exploits, combined with a sudden change in climate, are thought to have been responsible for its extinction about 10,000 years ago.

Illustrations Alan Male/Linden Artists

AFRICAN ELEPHANT

Loxodonta africana

(lox-a-DON-ta aff-ree-KA-na)

There are two different types, or subspecies, of **Loxodonta africana**. Both are distinguished by a third Latin name, so that the savanna elephant is known as **Loxodonta africana africana**, and the less common forest elephant as **Loxodonta africana cyclotis**.

The two subspecies vary in size and color, the savanna elephant being larger and darker with more hair.

SUBSPECIES:

FOREST ELEPHANT

SAVANNA ELEPHANT

AARDVARK

This family tree shows how the two species of elephants—the African and the Asian—are related to each other. It also shows that the rodentlike rock hyrax is a distant cousin of the elephants, along with the aardvark, the specialized ant-eating mammal of sub-Saharan Africa. The sirenians, marine mammals such as the dugong and manatee, are also distantly related. The elephant's evolutionary tale is among the most extraordinary in nature and, though the great age of the megaherbivores is gone, two or even three species remain.

ASIAN ELEPHANT

Elephas maximus

(ELL-ee-fass MAX-ee-muss)

There are four different subspecies of **Elephas maximus**, which vary slightly in size, skin color, and the size and shape of their ears.

The Ceylon elephant is known as **Elephas maximus maximus**, the Indian as **Elephas maximus bengalensis**, the Malaysian as **Elephas maximus indicus**, and the Sumatran as **Elephas maximus sumatranus**.

SUBSPECIES:

CEYLON ELEPHANT

INDIAN ELEPHANT

MALAYSIAN ELEPHANT

SUMATRAN ELEPHANT

ROCK HYRAX

PRIMITIVE
UNGULATES

657

ANATOMY:
THE ELEPHANT

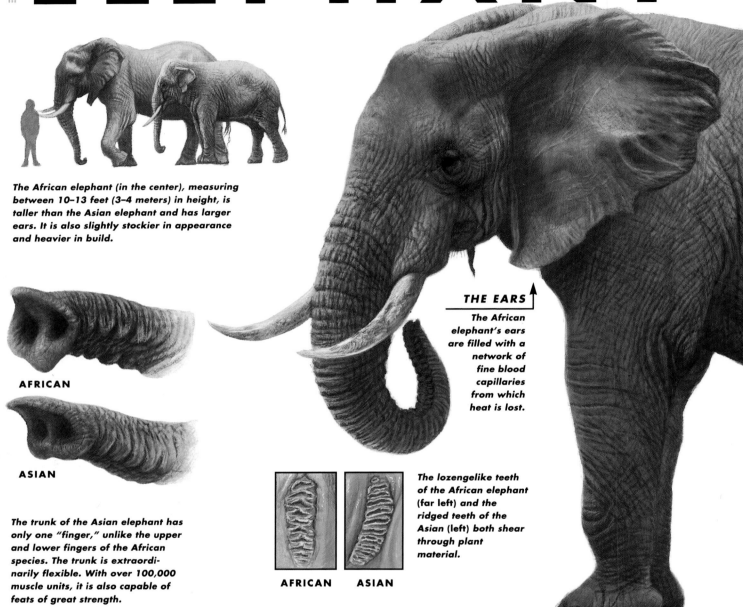

The African elephant (in the center), measuring between 10–13 feet (3–4 meters) in height, is taller than the Asian elephant and has larger ears. It is also slightly stockier in appearance and heavier in build.

AFRICAN

ASIAN

The trunk of the Asian elephant has only one "finger," unlike the upper and lower fingers of the African species. The trunk is extraordinarily flexible. With over 100,000 muscle units, it is also capable of feats of great strength.

THE EARS ↑

The African elephant's ears are filled with a network of fine blood capillaries from which heat is lost.

The lozengelike teeth of the African elephant (far left) and the ridged teeth of the Asian (left) both shear through plant material.

AFRICAN   ASIAN

Illustrations Mathew Hillier/Wildlife Art Agency

X
R
A
Y

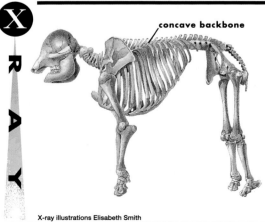

concave backbone

The most striking feature of the elephant's skeleton is its large skull, essential for supporting the animal's trunk and tusks. The African elephant has twenty-one ribs and a backbone that curves down, while the Asian species has one less rib and an upward-curving backbone.

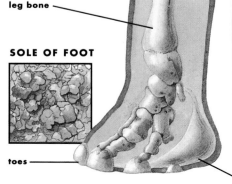

leg bone

SOLE OF FOOT

toes

Despite appearances, the elephant walks on its toes like a horse, its "heel" being just a pad of tissues. This is why the elephant is so light on its feet. The sole of the elephant's foot (inset) is covered by a thick layer of skin, which constantly renews itself.

fatty tissue pad

X-ray illustrations Elisabeth Smith

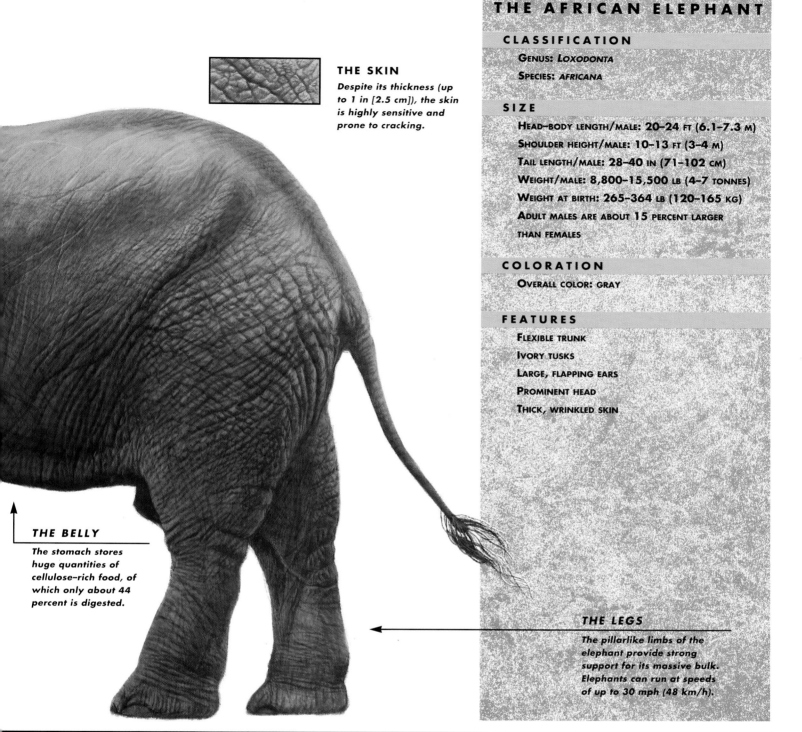

THE SKIN
Despite its thickness (up to 1 in [2.5 cm]), the skin is highly sensitive and prone to cracking.

FACT FILE

THE AFRICAN ELEPHANT

CLASSIFICATION
GENUS: *LOXODONTA*
SPECIES: *AFRICANA*

SIZE
HEAD–BODY LENGTH/MALE: 20–24 FT (6.1–7.3 M)
SHOULDER HEIGHT/MALE: 10–13 FT (3–4 M)
TAIL LENGTH/MALE: 28–40 IN (71–102 CM)
WEIGHT/MALE: 8,800–15,500 LB (4–7 TONNES)
WEIGHT AT BIRTH: 265–364 LB (120–165 KG)
ADULT MALES ARE ABOUT 15 PERCENT LARGER THAN FEMALES

COLORATION
OVERALL COLOR: GRAY

FEATURES
FLEXIBLE TRUNK
IVORY TUSKS
LARGE, FLAPPING EARS
PROMINENT HEAD
THICK, WRINKLED SKIN

THE BELLY
The stomach stores huge quantities of cellulose–rich food, of which only about 44 percent is digested.

THE LEGS
The pillarlike limbs of the elephant provide strong support for its massive bulk. Elephants can run at speeds of up to 30 mph (48 km/h).

Common to all African elephants and some Asian males, tusks are incisor teeth that continue to grow throughout the animal's life. Elephants use them to break off tree branches, for digging, and for warding off would-be attackers. They are the one true major source of ivory.

AFRICAN ELEPHANT

ASIAN ELEPHANT

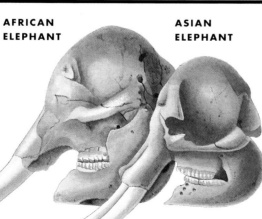

cross section of skull

The skull of the elephant is very large in comparison with its brain and is partly made up of a network of hollow cavities (left). These ensure that the skull is relatively light in weight. The jaws and teeth form the apparatus by which the elephant crushes the coarsest plant material.

THE MIGHTY VEGETARIANS

NEEDING LITTLE SLEEP, ELEPHANTS SPEND MOST OF THEIR LONG DAYS FORAGING FOR THE ENORMOUS AMOUNTS OF VEGETATION THEY NEED TO EAT IN ORDER TO SUSTAIN THEIR HUGE BULK

A s the largest living land mammals, elephants need plenty of space to live in. Using knowledge passed on to them by their mothers and grandmothers, they find their way over vast expanses of almost any kind of terrain in search of food and water. Their tremendously varied diet may consist of anything from grass and leaves to fruit and flowers and tree bark—even to mineral-rich soils.

African elephants, whose distribution ranges throughout most of the continent south of the Sahara, will travel several miles a day, if necessary, to find enough food to eat.

A DROP TO DRINK

Water is essential for drinking and bathing, and in the dry season African elephants may have to travel hundreds of miles to a river valley or swamp to find a watering hole. Once they have reached a suitable spot, they will remain there. In the wet season, when water is easily available, they can spread out; they might have home ranges as large as 1,200 square miles (3,108 square kilometers).

> GROUPS OF AFRICAN ELEPHANTS MAY TRAVEL VAST DISTANCES TO FIND ENOUGH TO EAT AND DRINK; ASIAN SPECIES ARE LESS NOMADIC

Asian elephants, on the other hand, usually do not have to move such great distances because they live in forests where many different types of vegetation are readily available and where the climate is more stable from season to season. One study found that the home range of some herds in the Malaysian rain forest was as small as 23 square miles (59 square kilometers).

Despite their size, elephants are surprisingly agile. Their solid and sturdy legs give them superb balance. They can walk over rocky ground with ease or silently pick their way through dense forest, their wide, spongy feet acting as shock absorbers for the weight of their bodies. Their long, flexible trunks are both sensitive and strong. With them, elephants can tear up grass, pull saplings out of the ground, or carefully pluck twigs and leaves from trees.

BUSY DAYS

Elephants spend most of their time eating, and sleep for only four or five hours a day, usually waking at fifteen-minute intervals to check for danger. During the very hot weather they seek out shade and spend the hottest part of the day resting under trees so that they don't overheat.

Steve Robinson/NHPA

Baobabs—tropical trees remarkable for their barrel-like trunks, which can measure as much as 30 feet (9 meters) in diameter—make a popular snack (above).

Family members are very close and touch each other frequently. These two African youngsters (left) touch trunks, while a family of Asian elephants (below) drinks together. Water holes are popular meeting spots, and often several families will gather at one.

Elephants live in close-knit family groups led by the oldest female. Within the group, individual elephants know their own social status and respond to others accordingly, forming unique relationships with one another. They communicate in several ways: by making rumbling sounds or trumpeting, by touching each other with their trunks, and by sniffing the scents of others. An individual elephant can be recognized by its smell or by the sound of its voice.

Most of an elephant's everyday activity, such as feeding, bathing, and sleeping, is carried out with other elephants. During the night families may split

> ELEPHANTS ARE HIGHLY SOCIAL ANIMALS, FORMING CLOSE-KNIT FAMILY GROUPS AND SPENDING MOST OF THEIR TIME IN COMPANY

up into smaller groups to sleep or to look for food. In the morning families will gather together again and move on to a new feeding area. Often several families will come together to form a herd so that they can travel safely in large numbers.

Groups of elephants sometimes come running, trumpeting excitedly, to greet old friends. This and other shows of "emotion" cannot help but remind us of ourselves—complex individuals who form close relationships with their families and friends. ∎

661

HABITATS

Once all elephants were probably forest-dwelling animals, but today they have adapted to many different habitats. Wild African elephants are distributed throughout sub-Saharan Africa, inhabiting woodland, savanna, and forest.

The two varieties of African elephants are classed according to where they live: The savanna elephant is found mainly on the African plains and in savanna woodland, and the smaller forest elephant lives in the forests of West Africa and the Congo basin.

The North African Atlas elephant, which was once tamed for domestic use, has now disappeared. This was a version of the African savanna elephant and, it is supposed, the elephant that Hannibal used to cross the Alps.

Asian elephants range from Bangladesh to Bhutan, Cambodia, China, and India, and through to

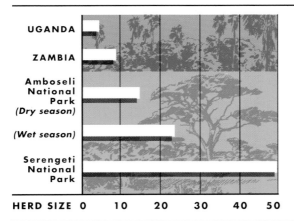

Mary Tracy/Jacana Ltd.

DISTRIBUTION

KEY

AFRICAN ELEPHANT

ASIAN ELEPHANT

The elephant is found throughout the Old World tropics, though its numbers are much reduced. The African elephant, now limited to land south of the Sahara, is most common in East and Central Africa, though colonies exist in Angola, Namibia, and South Africa.

The largest populations of Asian species can be found in predominantly rural Myanmar (formerly Burma) and Thailand. Smaller scattered populations are found in south and Southeast Asia.

On the march: Sunlight breaks through the dense forest canopy as these Asian elephants go in search of food.

Indonesia, Laos, West Malaysia, Myanmar, Sri Lanka, Thailand, and Vietnam. Most live in forests, but some also live on plains and in marshes.

There are about 40,000 wild Asian elephants, although some countries have fewer than a hundred. In addition, about 14,000 to 17,000 domesticated elephants work in Asia, mostly in logging, in places where machines cannot easily go.

THE SIZE OF AN ELEPHANT'S EARS REFLECTS ITS HABITAT: THE HOTTER THE CLIMATE, THE BIGGER ITS EARS, WHICH ARE BETTER FOR COOLING

Elephants need lots of living space because they only eat plants. Plants do not give as much energy as meat, so elephants have to graze over wide areas to find enough food for their needs. This is especially true in desert areas, where food is scarce.

The elephant is well adapted to survive in tropical climates. Its big ears have very fine veins, or capillaries, lying near the surface of the skin. The

HERD SIZE AND HABITAT

WOODLAND

SAVANNA

The size of an elephant herd is dependent on habitat. In general, the more fertile a habitat is, the larger the herd it can support. There are seasonal factors, too: Herds in Kenya's Amboseli National Park increase substantially in size during the more fruitful wet season.

UGANDA
ZAMBIA
Amboseli National Park (Dry season)
(Wet season)
Serengeti National Park

HERD SIZE   0   10   20   30   40   50

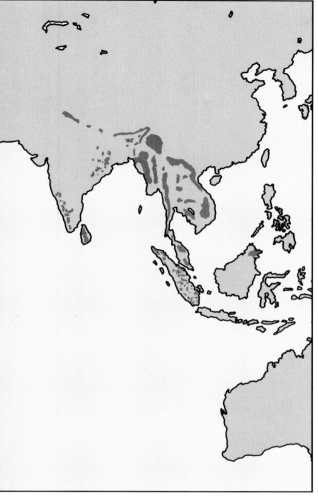

Robert Jacques/Jacana Ltd.

KEY FACTS

● In some areas of elephant habitat, the elephant's tree-destroying behavior allows sun-loving plants to flourish, thereby supporting a whole nonforest ecosystem.

● The baobab tree is richer in calcium and trace elements than any other tree. Only the elephant is capable of felling it.

● Elephants are found in climates with annual rainfalls ranging from 20–200 in (50 to 500 cm) and at altitudes ranging from 330 ft (100 m) to over 6,560 ft (2,000 m) above sea level.

all elephants carry seeds of their food plants to new places in their digestive systems. In fact, many tree seeds will not germinate, or begin to grow, unless an elephant has digested them first.

Elephants also improve their habitat for other creatures. Their trampling and rolling activities at water holes makes the holes stronger by compacting the walls, and the mud carried away on their bodies slowly enlarges the pools.

Where elephants have knocked down trees or dug to find minerals, the soil is loosened so that it can absorb the rain. In dry weather, elephants dig down to underground water supplies, which other animals can then use for drinking and bathing. ■

A herd of African elephants passes through woodland savanna in front of the snow-capped peak of Tanzania's Mount Kilimanjaro.

blood passes through these capillaries and is cooled down as the elephant flaps its ears back and forth. This helps the animal regulate the temperature of its body. In general, the hotter the habitat, the bigger the elephant's ears—this is why the African elephant has larger ears than the Asian species. Elephants also cool down by splashing themselves with water and mud from water holes.

INTREPID TRAVELERS

Although they cannot jump or gallop, elephants are extremely agile and can travel across almost any terrain. These heavy animals can climb steep slopes and tackle mountainous areas with ease.

The elephant's walking pace is about the same as human's, but they can run at a speed of up to 30 mph (48 km/h) and, because of their great size, bushes and shrubs are no obstacle to them. Surprisingly good swimmers, elephants cross rivers and lakes using their trunks as snorkels.

Though they are insatiable foragers, elephants often improve their habitat and, through their everyday activities, aid plant growth. For example,

FOOD AND FEEDING

Elephants eat grass and almost every part of trees and shrubs—leaves, fruit, flower buds, and even the woody branches, roots, and bark. But the exact composition of their diet depends upon the time of year and where they live.

Grass is the preferred food of African elephants; they pull it up by the roots and shake the soil free before eating it. It is difficult to study Asian elephants living in dense forests, but it is thought

ELEPHANTS USE THEIR FLEXIBLE TRUNKS AND STRONG, POINTED TUSKS AS TOOLS WHEN EATING

that they eat mostly bamboo, palms, fruit, climbers, and other forest plants.

The oldest female of the group knows where her family's favorite foods are to be found and when they will be ready to eat. In the right season, she will lead her family along time-honored paths in order to reach them.

Unfortunately, this migration often causes friction between elephants and farmers: The animals' traditional paths or "corridors" frequently bring them across farmland, where they will eat the farmers' crops. Just imagine what damage a herd of hungry elephants can do to a cornfield!

DIGGING IN

The elephant's trunk is invaluable. It is powerful enough to uproot saplings and snatch up huge clumps of grass, but, with its sensitive tip, it is also used for sniffing at branches, gently snapping off twigs, and delicately plucking off leaves and berries.

Tusks are used to dig up succulent tree roots

lying below the surface, and to dig into the ground to turn up mineral-rich soil. Because their trunks and tusks get in the way of their tongues, elephants can't lick at the mineral salts in the soil as other animals do. So they eat the soil, and even grind up rocks with their teeth, to extract the salts they need.

In order to find enough food to eat, elephants

Anatomically an extended upper lip, the trunk gives an elephant the skill it needs to handle a wide variety of foods.

Anup & Manuj Shah/Auscape International

EATING TREES

Elephants can cause severe damage to trees, particularly in the dry season when the grass becomes unappetizing. They will push trees over to reach the more succulent leaves, or strip and eat the bark of a baobab (as shown right) or acacia.

SEASONAL INTAKE

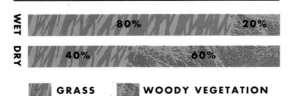

WET	80%	20%
DRY	40%	60%

▨ **GRASS**   ▨ **WOODY VEGETATION**

The diet of African elephants is more seasonal than that of Asian species. During the rains African elephants eat mostly grass, but in the dry season they must make do with less nutritious woody matter. Their total intake of food averages 450–600 lb (205–270 kg) a day in the rainy season, but only 330–375 lb (150–170 kg) when it is dry.

Illustration Alan Male/Linden Artists

need to graze and browse for about 18 to 20 hours a day, eating at daybreak, in the afternoon, and again in the middle of the night.

To process the huge quantity and wide variety of foods it eats, the elephant has a huge stomach, and its intestines are about 115 feet (35 meters) long. It takes 24 hours to digest each meal, but the digestion itself is very inefficient, and only around half of the food is actually used in the elephant's body; the rest is eliminated as waste in its dung. ■

Vivek Sinha/Survival Anglia

DRINKING

Elephant families can never be far from a water source, and during droughts they will travel hundreds of miles to find one. Their survival often depends on the oldest female's experience; she will lead the rest of the herd to water. They will then stay near the water source until the drought ends, rarely journeying farther than 15 miles (25 kilometers) away from it.

To drink, an elephant sucks water up into its trunk and squeezes the end shut. Then it puts its trunk into its mouth and lets the water gush down its throat. When using its trunk to aspirate water, it breathes only through its mouth.

Baby elephants need lots of practice to learn how to drink using their trunks, and when they are very young they will frequently drink with just their mouths, curling their trunks out of the way.

KEY FACTS

● Elephants can eat as much as 620 lb (280 kg) of food in a single day and drink up to 45 gal (170 l) water.

● Herd members eat at the same time, with almost the same rhythm, and prepare their food in the same way.

● Elephants can detect a source of water from several miles away.

● An elephant can suck up a bucketful of water with its trunk at one time.

SOCIAL STRUCTURE

Elephants are highly social, intelligent animals. They recognize each other as individuals, react to others according to their social standing, and seem to show real emotion toward one another.

MATERNAL INSTINCTS

The smallest social unit is the family group, made up of a mature female, who is the head of the family, one or several of her daughters and sisters, and the daughters' and sisters' own babies.

The size of the social group varies according to the season and the availability of food. Several family groups often come together to form a large group or herd; then, in the dry season when food is scarce, they separate into small groups to feed.

The leader of the herd is the oldest female—the matriarch—because she is most experienced. The sort of female-dominated society she heads is called matriarchal. If a calf or a sick adult is threatened by a predator, the rest of the group will enclose it in a protective circle; the matriarch will even risk her life to defend the herd.

Much of the knowledge that an elephant needs to survive is not instinctive but is learned by example

---

A GROUP OR HERD OF ELEPHANTS IS LED BY THE OLDEST FEMALE, CALLED THE MATRIARCH. OTHER HERD MEMBERS LEARN FROM HER EXPERIENCE

---

from the matriarch. Over several decades, in good and bad times, she will have followed age-old routes to find water and food. She will have had calves herself and much experience in rearing and defending them. She knows how to avoid danger and can lead the herd to sources of food at the right time of year. It is this vast knowledge and experience that the rest of the herd respects, making her the undisputed head of the group.

NEXT IN LINE

If the matriarch should die before her time—unless there is another experienced female to take her place—the herd may lose its vital knowledge. It may even break up because it has no strong leadership. In the usual pattern of events, though, the matriarch will lead the group until she is in her late 50s or 60s. Then her teeth begin to wear down and, because she cannot feed properly, she will gradually become weaker and eventually die. The next-ranking elephant, often her daughter, will take over her role, establishing her dominance over the other cows.

Females usually stay in the family group for the rest of their lives, but a bull calf will leave— sometimes unwillingly—in his early teens, often being chased away to prevent him from mating with the cows of his own family.

MALE SOCIETY

At first a bull calf may hang around on the fringes of the group, but eventually he will wander off on his own. He may meet other young males from time to time and indulge in mock fights to establish a pattern of dominance, but they will not stay together. Young males may learn by example from older bulls they meet, such as how to assert their dominance over other males. Only when they are looking to mate will adult bulls approach a herd and become involved in group activities. After mating, they leave to lead a solitary life once more.

Apart from trumpeting sounds, until recently it was thought that elephants were relatively silent. Scientists had long wondered how it was

MATRIARCH WITH YOUNG

As the oldest and most experienced female, the matriarch is the leader. She decides where the herd should travel, what they should eat and drink, and where they should rest.

Mathew Hillier/Wildlife Art Agency

THE ELEPHANT HERD

How individuals interrelate

BULL ELEPHANT
This bull approaches to look for a mate.

FAMILY GROUPS
When food is scarce, large herds may split up temporarily into small groups to feed.

FEMALE ELEPHANTS
The matriarch leads other females and their young.

ADOLESCENT BULL
This maturing male is tolerated for now but will soon be shunned by the rest of the herd to prevent it from mating with the young females. Although this action seems cruel, it means that inbreeding within a herd is avoided.

ELEPHANT CALLS

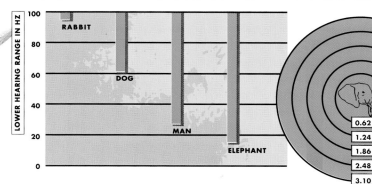

LOWER HEARING RANGE IN HZ

RABBIT — DOG — MAN — ELEPHANT

0.62
1.24
1.86
2.48
3.10

DISTANCE CALLS TRAVEL IN MILES

The chart shows the varying hearing ranges of different mammals, including man. The rabbit has a very high hearing range and can produce and hear only relatively high sounds. Dogs have a higher hearing range than man, but man can detect a wider range of sounds. Elephants have the lowest hearing range. They are able to hear and produce deep sounds of very low frequencies, called infrasounds, that are inaudible to humans.

Elephant infrasounds have a long wavelength, so they travel a long way. They can be heard by another elephant up to 3 miles (5 km) away.

667

that the animals seemed to know what was happening in other groups many miles away. They were seen mysteriously to change direction to avoid feeding in the same area as another group, respond in a distressed manner to another family's destruction many miles away, or just stand with their heads up and their ears spread

---

ELEPHANTS COMMUNICATE WITH ONE ANOTHER IN SEVERAL WAYS: BY TOUCH, SIGHT, AND SCENT, AND ALSO BY MAKING VARIOUS SOUNDS AND RUMBLES

---

out as if they were listening, even when no other animal was in sight.

A scientist named Katherine Payne solved the mystery. She had studied the way that whales called to each other on a wavelength so low that humans could not hear it. While watching some Asian elephants at a zoo, she felt a kind of vibration through her body and wondered whether there was any connection between this vibration and her work on whale communication.

A NEW DISCOVERY

Payne recorded elephant vibrations at the zoo and then speeded them up ten times to bring the sounds into the range of human hearing. She discovered that the elephants were indeed communicating with each other at a frequency far too low for human ears. These rumblings were being produced in the animals' throats.

Later work with elephants in the wild established that there are special rumbles for special purposes. When the tapes were played back to the elephants, they responded in an appropriate way—they replied to a greeting call or changed the group's direction. The rumble of a female in season

AMAZING

THE GREETING CEREMONY

Sometimes when two groups of elephants meet, or when a group rejoins a herd, there is great excitement and a big commotion. There are special calls, flapping of ears, fondling with trunks, and dropping of dung (probably to establish a group scent). Individuals will often put their trunks into each other's mouths to say hello. Such friendly "bond groups" may be distantly related, or, perhaps they came about when one family group split into two.

AT THE WATERING HOLE

The watering hole acts as a meeting place and an information center. By examining different scents, individuals can tell which elephants have visited the water before them and how long ago it was.

Mathew Hillier/Wildlife Art Agency

brought a bull elephant toward the tape player, pacing in the special "head high" way that a bull in mating condition uses when coming toward a cow.

A surprisingly long list of calls made by savanna elephants has since been put together, but there is still much work to be done on this subject, particularly among forest and Asian elephants.

ON THE BREEZE

Elephants' trunks are particularly sensitive to both smell and touch. The air is full of scent messages, and elephants often stand with their trunks upraised, sniffing them in. It is impossible to know how much information is picked up in this way.

Sick or injured elephants are comforted in their stress by the touch of gentle trunks and soothing sounds. Mother elephants stay near their calves and are constantly feeling and reassuring them.

Elephants communicate with their bodies in other ways. If they are angry or alarmed, they hold

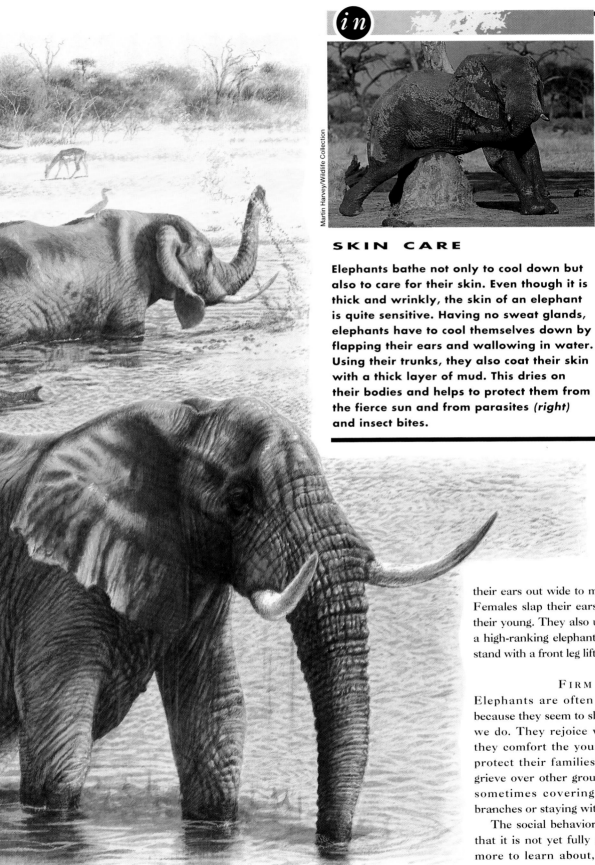

Martin Harvey/Wildlife Collection

SKIN CARE

Elephants bathe not only to cool down but also to care for their skin. Even though it is thick and wrinkly, the skin of an elephant is quite sensitive. Having no sweat glands, elephants have to cool themselves down by flapping their ears and wallowing in water. Using their trunks, they also coat their skin with a thick layer of mud. This dries on their bodies and helps to protect them from the fierce sun and from parasites *(right)* and insect bites.

WARBLE FLY

This fly lays its eggs under an elephant's skin. The larvae feed on the flesh and then hatch out.

LEECH

Jungle leeches attach themselves to Asian elephants and suck their blood through their skin.

TICK

Ticks hook their legs and bury their heads into the skin to suck blood, which makes their bodies swell.

Illustrations Elisabeth Smith

their ears out wide to make themselves look bigger. Females slap their ears against their heads to call their young. They also use "intention movement": if a high-ranking elephant is ready to move on, it will stand with a front leg lifted to tell the others to go.

FIRM FRIENDS

Elephants are often compared with humans because they seem to show the same emotions that we do. They rejoice when greeting old friends, they comfort the young and the sick, and they protect their families from danger. They even grieve over other group members that have died, sometimes covering their bodies with leafy branches or staying with them for several days.

The social behavior of elephants is so complex that it is not yet fully understood. There is much more to learn about, and to learn from, these magnificent and intelligent creatures. ∎

LIFE CYCLE

The cooperation of individual elephants within a herd sees baby elephants successfully into their teens, young adults into maturity, and adult females into ripe old age.

When a male is ready to mate, he will become very aggressive. During this time, a bull will fight with other bulls, sometimes to the death, to win the chance to mate with a female. Mating is preceded by much touching, rumbling, and twining of trunks. The bull mounts the cow from behind with his front legs stretched along her back. Then the herd breaks

MATING IS A SOCIAL EVENT, TAKING PLACE AMONG THE HERD. BULLS WILL FIGHT OTHER BULLS FOR SUPREMACY AND THE PRIVILEGE OF MATING WITH A COW IN ESTRUS

into a noisy frenzy, called the mating pandemonium. If another bull is nearby, this will call him to the scene, but he must then fight to mate with the cow. The strongest bull will be the last to mate. He stays with her for a few days to keep other bulls at bay.

Usually a single calf is born, about 22 months later for an African elephant, or 21 months later for an Asian elephant. The calf, which weighs about 220 pounds (100 kilograms) and is about 3 feet (less than a meter) tall, can usually stand on its

AMAZING FACTS

Steve Turner/OSF

MUSTH

Musth (pronounced *must*) is an unexplained and little-studied phenomenon where an elephant's temporal glands—situated on each cheek between the eye and the ear—periodically secrete a dark, strong-smelling fluid. These glands are rarely active in Asian female elephants, although they are in African females. Musth is usually linked with the urge to mate, but elephants also reproduce outside this time. Musth bulls are extremely aggressive and many keepers have been killed by musth bulls in captivity.

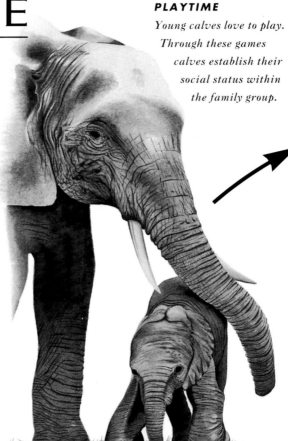

PLAYTIME
Young calves love to play. Through these games calves establish their social status within the family group.

THE NEWBORN CALF
takes its first wobbly steps, staying close to its mother. She remains in constant touch with the baby, gently reassuring it with her trunk.

Alan Male/Linden Artists

THE BULL MOUNTS
a female in heat, supporting his weight on his hind legs as mating takes place. An excited commotion then breaks out among the rest of the herd.

THE BABYSITTER

A young female acts as a babysitter for a calf to protect it from danger. Here the female stands in a defensive posture at the approach of a hungry lioness.

in SIGHT

ELEPHANT GRAVEYARDS

Legends often tell of secret places where elephants go to die. There is no evidence that these "graveyards" exist, but why, then, have piles of elephant bones been found in certain places? There are several possible explanations. In times of drought, dying elephants often migrate to swamps and rivers in search of water and food. Several may starve there or may be too weak to climb out of the mud again. Or they may be sites of mass slaughter by hunters: In the past, African tribesmen drove herds of elephants into a deep gorge and killed them for meat.

FIGHTING RIVALS

When they have the urge to mate, adult bulls become very aggressive. They will fight with any other bull they meet, wrestling with their tusks.

own within half an hour. It is totally dependent on the care it receives from the rest of the herd.

The calf suckles from two teats between its mother's front legs and continues to do so until it is about two years old. It will try to pick at grasses after a few months, but baby elephants find it difficult to manage their trunks at first.

Male calves need twice as much food as females in order to reach maturity, and because of this bull calves are the first to die in times of food shortage.

Young calves often play together, developing the skills they will need as adults, such as butting heads and charging. Playing continues for longer with male calves than females and is used to establish rank among the males.

STICKING TOGETHER

Young females usually stay with their families for the rest of their lives, helping to care for the calves. In this way they learn how to care for their own young. These babysitters will fiercely defend the calves in their care against rhinos, lions, cheetahs, hyenas, and leopards.

Elephants may reach the grand age of sixty-five or seventy before they die. Other herd members will stay close by to comfort a dying elephant and will guard the body for hours afterward. ■

VICTIMS OF VANITY

FOR SOME THIRTY-EIGHT MILLION YEARS, ELEPHANTS ROAMED ACROSS WILD LANDS IN RELATIVE SAFETY. NOW, OVER THE COURSE OF A BRIEF SNATCH OF TIME, THEY HAVE COME UNDER THREAT OF EXTINCTION. THEIR FUTURE LIES ENTIRELY IN OUR HANDS

There was a time, when the human population was a fraction of what it is today, when the world's wild lands stretched unbroken to the horizons, and when being a huge vegetarian animal was a successful way of life. The endless savannas and extensive forests provided plenty of food, water, and space for the roaming herds.

SQUEEZED OUT

Today, with expanding human populations, elephants are pressed on every side by our ever-growing demand on the land. Great savannas are now split up by roads and railroads; reservoirs replace forest valleys; more and more land is claimed for crops and grazing animals; villages and cities expand and eat up the land. The space that elephants need is no longer there, and the long-established elephant corridors—yearly migration

---

ELEPHANTS NEED PLENTY OF SPACE TO ROAM AND GRAZE. WHEN THEY ARE RESTRICTED TO PROTECTED AREAS, THEY CAN DEVASTATE THE LANDSCAPE

---

routes—are interrupted and blocked. In India it is thought that the human pressure on wild lands has increased by 40 percent in the last twenty years.

Even the usually effective policy of creating protected areas is problematic when elephants are involved. These huge animals can damage habitats when they are restricted to limited areas. For example, in the Tvaso National Park in Kenya, vast areas of landscape have been devastated by elephants with their massive food requirements.

By far the most serious threat to the elephant, however, is the ivory trade. Ivory is simply elephant tusk, and it has been treasured for centuries as a suitable material for carving into intricate objects. Added to the ever-present problem of habitat loss in the 1980s, the trade in ivory threatened to extinguish the elephant.

In the modern world the killing is easy. Four-wheel drive vehicles carry hunters with powerful rifles into the wild and elephants are easily shot from a distance. When one elephant is killed or injured the others tend to stay with it rather than flee, so whole groups can be killed at one time.

Slaughtered for their tusks, their bodies left to rot where they fall, elephants have declined in numbers. The world has become familiar with images of dead elephants with their tusks hacked from their mouths and of baby elephants left to starve when their mothers are killed. In Africa the number of elephants fell from 1,300,000 to 600,000 during the 1980s; in fact, it was estimated that an

Dr. Norman Myers/Bruce Coleman Ltd.

More people are now aware that the trade in ivory trinkets, such as that of Gabon (right), involves the cruel slaughter of African elephants (above).

Christian Zuber/Bruce Coleman Ltd.

THEN & NOW

The map below shows the former and current distributions of African and Asian elephants.

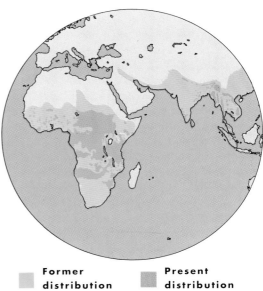

■ Former distribution   ■ Present distribution

Elephants have disappeared from
- the Middle East, Pakistan, China, Java
- South Africa and parts of East Africa

Scattered populations remain in
- India and Southeast Asia
- most of West Africa

This chart shows world trade in ivory and East African exports. From 1960, figures for African exports are unreliable because of political unrest. From 1975, CITES regulated the trade. This led to illegal traders selling off stock and, around 1980, the demand for ivory fell.

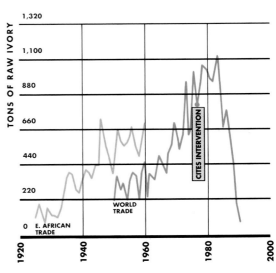

673

average of 2,000 elephants were killed for their tusks every week during those ten years.

By the late 1980s concern was rising everywhere. Many African nations were investing large amounts of money to fight poachers, but elephant populations still continued to fall; in Kenya, numbers fell from 130,000 in 1973 to 16,000 in 1989.

IVORY INFERNO

In 1989 the Kenyan president, Daniel T. Moi, publicly burned 13 tons of confiscated ivory. With increased public awareness, the United States and several European countries banned the import of ivory. Even though some African countries were having some success in protecting elephants from slaughter—numbers in Zimbabwe rose from 30,000 in 1979 to 45,000 in 1989—the international pressure was mounting to stop the ivory trade altogether.

From 1975 to 1989 the ivory trade was regulated under CITES—the Convention on International Trade in Endangered Species—where permits were required for international trading. This helped, but it wasn't enough. In October 1989, however, the African elephant was placed in Appendix 1 of CITES, which means that it was protected and trade in elephant produce was banned.

UPHOLDING THE LAW

At first the ban worked. Japan, which had previously been one of the main importers of ivory, enforced the ban vigorously, prosecuting traders who tried to bring ivory into the country. Actions on a smaller scale also had an effect. People in the west became informed as a result of conservation groups.

OUT OF ACTION

The closeness of people to elephants often causes problems. Since 1992, elephants around Lake Kariba in Zimbabwe have been suffering from trunk paralysis. The animals cannot feed or drink properly and are slowly starving to death. Scientists suspect that lead pollution is to blame. Lake Kariba is one of Zimbabwe's biggest tourist attractions, and discarded batteries, gasoline from boat engines, and fishing weights all add lead to the environment there. Scientists are hoping that the lead in the lake will soon be reduced so that elephant suffering will stop.

Elephants occasionally catch rabies from dog bites and, though this is rarely fatal, foot-and-mouth disease from cattle.

Cliff Venner/Panos Pictures

ENDANGERED SPECIES

DAMS IN INDIA: THE DANGERS FACING ASIAN ELEPHANTS

Water is one of Earth's most precious resources: All living things need fresh water to survive. By the turn of the century, however, the world's demand for water may increase by as much as 200 percent.

The greatest demand for water is for irrigation, especially in hot countries where drought can lead to the failure of crops—and to disaster. One solution is to build dams to control the flow of rivers.

THE POWER OF NATURE

By trapping water flowing down from mountains, dams form reservoirs and thereby guarantee a regular supply of fresh water for people and crops; yields have been known to increase ten times as a result of regular irrigation. The water in the reservoir, running out through the dam, can also be used to generate hydroelectric power, which is one of the least polluting ways to generate energy.

Dams can help local wildlife, too. In India's Western Ghats—a mountain range in the southwest—reservoirs provide

ELEPHANTS AND OTHER WILDLIFE CANNOT GET OUT OF CANALS IF THE SIDES ARE TOO STEEP. MANY DROWN.

CONSERVATION MEASURES

If the building of canals and dams is halted to protect wildlife, local people will inevitably suffer. Yet populations of Asian elephants and other animals are being affected.

Construction projects, such as Parambi-kulam-Aliyar in the Tamil Nadu and Kerala states, are now taking wildlife conservation into consideration, yet the needs of local people and wildlife sometimes conflict.

regular watering holes for wild elephants in an otherwise dry land.

When land is taken up to build reservoirs, however, many people have to move their homes. Wildlife in the area is displaced also or severely disrupted.

BLOCKING THE WAY

Elsewhere in the Western Ghats, elephant migration routes have been interrupted by water-carrying pipes; and steep-sided, fast-flowing canals have had an even worse effect: Elephants falling into them have been washed away and drowned, along with deer and even tigers. Some elephants have been rescued—pulled out by domesticated elephants—when they have gotten caught up against ramps at the entrances to tunnels, but these animals were the lucky ones.

With the drowning of both river valley habitats and the animals themselves, dams and reservoirs are a mixed blessing for wildlife in southern India.

John Mackinnon/ICCE Photolibrary

- More ramps are built at the entrances of tunnels to prevent animals from being washed away and drowned.

- Canals are constructed with shallower sides so that wildlife will not become trapped.

- Water channels are fenced off to keep animals from falling in; but, like water pipes, fencing disrupts elephant migratory routes.

Gunter Ziesler/Bruce Coleman Ltd.

ELEPHANTS IN DANGER

THE CHART BELOW SHOWS HOW THE INTERNATIONAL UNION FOR THE CONSERVATION OF NATURE (IUCN) CLASSIFIES THE STATUS OF AFRICAN AND ASIAN ELEPHANTS:

AFRICAN ELEPHANT	VULNERABLE
ASIAN ELEPHANT	ENDANGERED

ENDANGERED MEANS THAT THE ANIMAL IS IN DANGER OF EXTINCTION AND ITS SURVIVAL IS UNLIKELY UNLESS STEPS ARE TAKEN TO SAVE IT. *VULNERABLE* INDICATES THAT THE ANIMAL IS LIKELY TO MOVE INTO THE ENDANGERED CATEGORY IF THINGS CONTINUE AS THEY ARE.

With the difficulty of trading and a drop in demand, the price of ivory fell. In Somalia, within a few months of the ban, the price had dropped from one hundred dollars a kilo to just five. In Africa and elsewhere ivory carvers went out of business.

BLACK MARKET

In recent months, however, there has been growing concern about the effectiveness of the ban. Though much of the concern is based on rumor rather than fact, there are definite signs that all is not well. In early 1993, for example, Tanzania's wildlife department gloomily reported that its antipoaching units were "fighting a losing battle."

For poaching to be worthwhile, somebody must be buying the ivory. At present, sales are booming in Addis Ababa, Ethiopia, and it is believed that this is partly fed by the poaching and illegal import of tusks from neighboring countries. Ivory is also seen

THE TRADE IN IVORY STILL CONTINUES TODAY DESPITE AN INTERNATIONAL BAN. IN SOME AFRICAN COUNTRIES, POACHING IS ACTUALLY INCREASING

on sale in many parts of the Far East; again, this may be fueled by poached African ivory. This does not account for all the ivory being poached, and it seems likely that ivory traders are illegally importing ivory and stockpiling it in the hope that the trade will start again in the future.

As long as ivory has a high value, there will be money in trading it, and as long as there is a

675

ALONGSIDE MAN

ELEPHANTS AT WORK

For over 5,000 years, Asian elephants have been domesticated. Today they are used to carry heavy loads, especially in places that are too muddy for vehicles. They work mainly in the timber industry, felling trees and carrying logs away. Magnificently dressed, elephants grace state ceremonies and religious festivals; they also play an important role in tourism, which creates valuable revenue.

When they are about ten years old, the elephants start training with mahouts, who become very fond of their charges. The beasts are retired at fifty-five.

demand for it, there will be a good price. Protected areas will help keep some elephants safe, but in the end the most likely way for the trade—legal or illegal—to end would be for demand to fall off.

In India, one of the last countries to have a sizable Asian elephant population (around 20,000 out of about 46,000 across Asia), the ivory trade has had less effect than it has in Africa. In Asian elephants only the bulls have tusks, and these are relatively small, so the Asian populations have not suffered as badly. Even so, habitat destruction and ivory hunting of the past have already decreased Asian populations.

In India, as in Africa, elephants that live near agricultural areas sometimes become "crop raiders." The damage can be devastating for small farmers and their families, so it is not surprising that such elephants get killed: They are either shot or, in some cases, electrocuted by fencing.

Asian elephants, dressed in splendor, take part in an elephant march in Kerala, India.

In Kenya's ivory inferno of 1989, confiscated ivory was publicly burned.

Fortunately there are solutions. Milder electric fencing, using shocks that do not harm, has proved successful. Some herds have been driven to new habitats in India and elsewhere, though several elephants have found their way back again.

NEW ROUTES

To link isolated elephant habitats, man-made corridors are now being set up. Their aim is to help elephants travel freely over wide areas, avoiding contact with farmland. These corridors are anything from a bridge across a canal to land migration routes, where an area of land is left free for elephants to travel through.

In Sri Lanka, for example, a protected strip of land following the Mahaweli River Basin now links two isolated national parks, the Somawathiya National Park in the north of the country and the Minneriya Giritale Nature Reserve in the south. Elephants and other animals have more space to

> CONSERVATION OF ASIAN ELEPHANTS IS NOW UNDER WAY. HERDS MAY TRAVEL FREELY THROUGH AREAS OF PROTECTED LAND THAT LINK MIGRATORY ROUTES

roam and are free to travel in safety between the two protected areas, with plenty of food and water available en route.

The elephant has a part to play in the lives of many people. There is no doubt that it can continue to do so, but only worldwide efforts can guarantee its survival. Is the future of the largest land animal in the hands of the world's most arrogant? ∎

INTO THE FUTURE

The protection given to elephants in some countries before and since the ban on ivory trade has led to population increases but, unfortunately, this success brings problems with it. In Zimbabwe, numbers in some national parks have reached levels where the elephants are causing damage. In the past, elephants were able to move on from exhausted feeding areas, giving the vegetation time to recover; but when the animals are closed in, habitats come under pressure.

Zimbabwe has culled hundreds of elephants in the past but has recently tried moving them from Gonarezhu National Park, where drought has

PREDICTION

PROJECT ELEPHANT

A national initiative called Project Elephant is now being planned to safeguard wild elephants in India. If the plan is implemented, it should guarantee the elephant's survival there, even if it continues to decline elsewhere in Asia.

depleted food sources and added to the population problems, to other parks and preserves. However, there is a persistent fear that if the number of elephants is not reduced, the land may never recover.

Zimbabwe and other African countries promoting culling make the point that none of the dead animal goes to waste: The hide is used to make leather goods and the meat feeds local people. In Gonarezhu, the drought is so severe that villagers have been reduced to eating worms and nuts. In this way, culling aids human welfare.

VALUABLE RESOURCES

There is no doubt that the future of the elephant is an unpredictable one, both in Africa and in Asia. But although it is impossible to predict future trends, it seems likely that numbers will continue to stay stable, at least in the African countries that have sizable populations.

In the long term, however, the future of the elephant depends on people believing that the elephant is worth preserving—as a tourist attraction and money-earner in national parks, as domesticated stock used for work, and as a wild animal that has, like us, the right to live. ■

CITES 1994

At the 1994 meeting of CITES, a debate of national versus international agendas took place. Many nations would like to have a controlled resumption of international ivory trading. The sale of ivory could help African people move toward the kind of wealthy lifestyle that Westerners enjoy. However, the concern among conservationists is that illegal poaching will continue anyway. As it stands, countries that would like to sell ivory cannot prove that a reopened trade would not jeopardize elephants in other areas.

STAR ATTRACTIONS

Recent studies in several African countries have shown that if local people become involved in national parks and reap the benefits of the money raised by tourism, poaching for ivory declines. It is a story that is often repeated in conservation: Improve the lot of the local people and you improve the lot of the wildlife. Tourists on safari can now watch elephants in their natural habitat; they can also ride on the backs of them as they observe other animals.

In Asia, elephant training centers are major tourist attractions. Visitors are given a display of how the elephants work, as well as the chance to meet the elephants face to face and ride on their backs.

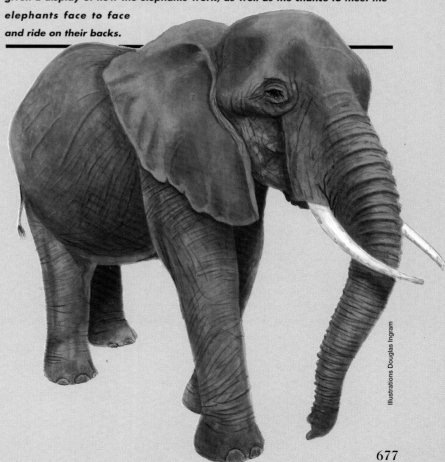

Illustrations Douglas Ingram

677

LUPINE FOXES

Foxes belong to the mammal order Carnivora and the dog family, Canidae. Other canids include:

WOLVES

JACKALS

COYOTE

DINGO

DOMESTIC DOG

BUSH DOG

RACCOON DOG

Gunter Ziesler/Bruce Coleman Ltd.

KINGS OF THE WILD FRONTIER

FOXES ARE VERY, VERY VERSATILE: WHILE MOST HAVE THE FLEXIBILITY TO ADAPT DAILY TO NEW SITUATIONS, SOME HAVE BECOME PHYSICALLY ADAPTED TO SURVIVE IN THE MOST TESTING HABITATS ON EARTH

In the heart of the Sahara, where the midday sun can heat the desert sand to temperatures of over 195°F (90°C), the little fennec fox has solved the problem of walking over the equivalent of a scalding hot radiator by developing fur-padded feet. The fur provides insulation against the heat and improves the fox's grip on the dry, shifting sand. So a fennec can step outside at noon in one of the hottest places on earth without being fried alive. Up in the frozen

wastes of the high Arctic, meanwhile, the arctic fox has acquired the same adaptation for padding over sheet ice and powder snow. The fur improves its grip and acts as a barrier against the cold, enabling the fox to take a stroll in one of the coldest places on earth without succumbing to frostbite.

These animals have more specific adaptations to cope with their extremely demanding habitats, but in many ways they are almost identical. Resilient, active opportunists, prepared to eat almost anything,

679

The distinctive bat-eared fox (below)
is highly adapted to locate insect prey.

Deeble & Stone/Survival Anglia

their ability to thrive in such dramatically different environments exemplifies the astonishing versatility of the foxes, which are among the most widespread and successful of all the carnivores.

THE DOG FAMILY

The origins of foxes are still uncertain. They are all canids—members of the dog family—and were first grouped on the basis of their size and appearance rather than any more scientific characteristics. They are all agile, lithe animals with long legs and long, bushy tails, narrow muzzles, keen senses, and acute intelligence—but the same is true of dogs, wolves, and jackals. In fact, the distinction between a dog and a fox is subtle, and recent studies indicate that there is a line clean through the group known as the foxes.

The arctic fox has shorter limbs than its southern
cousins; this gives it a more compact appearance.

Ian Beames/Ardea

 SIGHT

FALKLAND ISLANDER

The only wild canid species that has actually become extinct in historical times is the Falkland Island wolf, *Dusicyon australis*. First described in 1689, this relatively large animal had a broad, doglike muzzle and may be more closely related to the coyote than to the South American foxes. It occurred only on the Falklands, where it lived mainly by scavenging along the seashore for dead seals, fish, and seabirds, as well as preying on live penguins.

With the arrival of European settlers and their livestock, this wolf was soon perceived as a threat and persecuted accordingly. By the time Darwin visited the islands in HMS *Beagle* in 1833, it was already becoming scarce. A ready market for its thick pelt plus an official price on its head hastened its decline, and the last known wild specimen was killed in 1876.

On one side of the line are the red fox and its allies in the genus *Vulpes*, called the vulpine foxes. These animals share a number of habits, as well as a concavity of the frontal bones between the eyes. On the other side of the line are the South American foxes of the genus *Dusicyon*, such as the crab-eating fox and the colpeo fox, which have flat frontal bones. This feature, plus some aspects of behavior, places them closer to the lupine (wolflike) dogs, which have convex frontal bones.

This leaves a number of species that are neither *Vulpes* nor *Dusicyon*, having been classified in their own genera for various reasons. These include the fennec and the arctic fox, which are set apart from the rest because of their adaptations for extreme environments. Recent studies suggest that both species in fact derive from the vulpines, and that the arctic fox is a recent offshoot of the red fox line, diverging one or two million years ago. So some zoologists have proposed reclassifying them in the genus *Vulpes*—but this is not widely approved.

There is no such debate over the unique bat-eared fox. Although superficially foxy, this native of the African savannas has abandoned the opportunist habits of its ancestors: It feeds mainly on termites and beetles, locating them with its large ears and crushing them with its cheek teeth. Small insects can make frustrating prey for a relatively big animal, but the bat-eared fox has extra molar teeth and special jaw muscles that enable it to pulp termites at the rate of more than three chews per second.

The bat-eared fox's ancestors probably split from the main canid line five or six million years ago, in the wake of climatic changes that led to an expansion of the grasslands that form its main habitat today. This was also the period when the vulpine and lupine lines began to diversify. The lupines gave rise to a number of predatory, fast-running, pack-hunting canids—the wolves and wild dogs—but it also generated the South American foxes, or *zorros*. Like their vulpine counterparts, the South American foxes prey on small animals and have no reason to hunt in packs or run fast. Instead they tend to hunt alone, by stealth. Small vertebrates are a favorite prey, but most foxes will eat almost anything, including insects, worms, fruits, nuts, and carrion.

This tendency to small-scale feeding is the reason why, regardless of their origins, all foxes tend to look alike. Agility and precision take precedence over speed and brute power, and foxes are less bulky than dogs of similar length. Their jaws are narrower for rooting in crevices, and they can process a wide variety of foods, having a full battery of tooth types. The muzzle has to be long to house these teeth, and this reduces the force that the jaw muscles can exert. So by comparison with a cat, which has a short but powerful jaw, a fox can kill only relatively small prey. As a formula for adaptability, however, it has proved unbeatable, which is why the foxes are among the most successful of all mammals today. ■

DARWIN'S FOX

The South American foxes have been so little studied that even the number of species is open to doubt. For example, when Charles Darwin landed on the island of Chiloe, off the Chilean coast, he noticed a small fox watching the landing party. Armed with his geological hammer, he approached the hapless animal and killed it with a single blow. Stuffed and mounted, it was ultimately exhibited in London and given the scientific name *Dusicyon fulvipes*.

Later it became clear that, although smaller, Darwin's fox was very similar to the colpeo fox, *Pseudalopex culpaeus*. Common sense suggested that it was merely a small island race of the colpeo, and it lost its status as a separate species. In 1990, however, small foxes resembling Darwin's fox were reported on the Chilean mainland, reviving the separatist argument. The issue is still not resolved, and similar confusion surrounds at least two other races—or possibly species—of South American foxes.

B/W illustrations Ruth Grewcock

THE FOXES' FAMILY TREE

The family Canidae is divided into lupines and vulpines. The former includes wolves, jackals, wild dogs, the maned wolf, and the genus Pseudalopex. The vulpines comprise the genus Vulpes plus the arctic and fennec foxes. The bat-eared fox probably stems from the common ancestors of both dogs and foxes.

COLPEO FOX

Pseudalopex culpaeus
(*soo-dah-LO-pecks cul-PIE-uss*)

Typical of the seven surviving species of South American foxes, the colpeo fox ranges south down the Pacific seaboard of South America from Peru to Tierra del Fuego, from sea level to altitudes of up to 14,760 ft (4,500 m) in the Andes. An adaptable, opportunist hunter, it feeds mainly on rabbits and small rodents.

MANED WOLF

LUPINE DOGS
(GENUS *CANIS*)

FAMILY CANIDAE
(DOGS AND FOXES)

ARCTIC FOX

Alopex lagopus
(AL-o-pecks lag-O-pus)

Protected by its superb winter coat, the arctic fox can tolerate months of subzero conditions. With a circumpolar range extending from the northern tundra to the Arctic pack ice, it has the most northerly distribution of any land mammal except the polar bear.

VULPINE FOXES (GENUS *VULPES*)

FENNEC FOX

Fennecus zerda
(FEN-eh-cuss ZERD-ah)

The smallest of the foxes, the delicate fennec is highly adapted to survive the burning heat and drought of the Sahara. Its large ears act as very efficient heat radiators; they also detect the slightest sound that might lead it to the small desert rodents and insects that form the bulk of its diet.

BAT-EARED FOX

Otocyon megalotis
(ot-o-SIE-on mega-LO-tiss)

Uniquely among canids, the bat-eared fox feeds almost entirely upon insects—principally harvester termites—and has evolved specialized dentition and jaw musculature to cope with its prey. Since it can thrive only where the harvester termites are numerous, it is restricted to the savanna grasslands of tropical Africa.

Main illustrations Simon Turvey/Wildlife Art Agency

ANATOMY:
THE ARCTIC FOX

THE WINTER COAT

consists of 70 percent thick underfur and 30 percent long guard hairs—a combination that, for fur, provides a level of insulation unparalleled among animals, enabling the arctic fox to sleep on ice at –94°F (–70°C) for an hour before feeling chilled.

THE EARS

are small and rounded to reduce heat loss and are probably less sensitive than the larger ears of southern species.

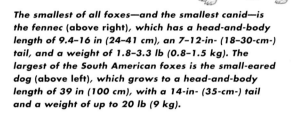

The smallest of all foxes—and the smallest canid—is the fennec (above right), which has a head-and-body length of 9.4–16 in (24–41 cm), an 7–12-in- (18–30-cm-) tail, and a weight of 1.8–3.3 lb (0.8–1.5 kg). The largest of the South American foxes is the small-eared dog (above left), which grows to a head-and-body length of 39 in (100 cm), with a 14-in- (35-cm-) tail and a weight of up to 20 lb (9 kg).

THE MUZZLE

is shorter than that of most foxes to reduce its surface area and heat loss, but it is still long enough to contain a multipurpose set of teeth and an extended nasal cavity to give an acute sense of smell.

PAWS

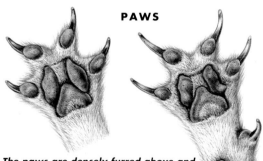

The paws are densely furred above and below to keep out the cold, enabling the arctic fox to range for hours over the ice without discomfort.

THE LEGS

are shorter than those of other foxes, reducing surface area and heat loss. The arctic fox lacks the lithe grace of species such as the red fox.

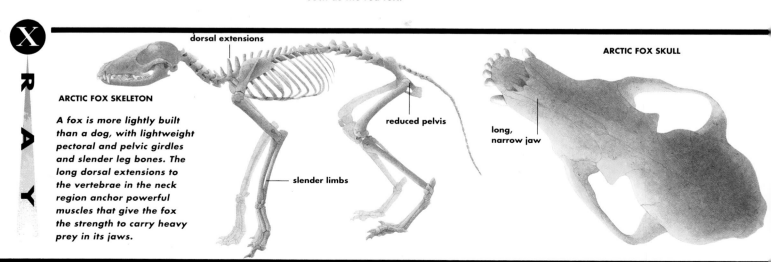

X

R A Y

dorsal extensions

ARCTIC FOX SKULL

reduced pelvis

long, narrow jaw

ARCTIC FOX SKELETON

A fox is more lightly built than a dog, with lightweight pectoral and pelvic girdles and slender leg bones. The long dorsal extensions to the vertebrae in the neck region anchor powerful muscles that give the fox the strength to carry heavy prey in its jaws.

slender limbs

X-ray illustrations Elisabeth Smith

SUMMER COAT

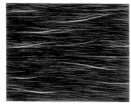

SUMMER COAT

BLUE COAT

Most arctic foxes are pure white in winter, molting in summer to a smoky gray brown with white underparts; but in coastal areas where winter snow cover is patchy—particularly in Iceland—some individuais have bluish gray coats that molt to uniform chocolate brown in summer. This blue form has been cultivated in captivity but is relatively uncommon in the wild.

THE ARCTIC FOX

CLASSIFICATION

GENUS: *ALOPEX*

SPECIES: *LAGOPUS*

SIZE

HEAD–BODY LENGTH: 22 IN (55 CM)

TAIL LENGTH: 12 IN (30 CM)

AVERAGE WEIGHT/MALE: 8.3 LB (3.8 KG)

AVERAGE WEIGHT/FEMALE: 6.8 LB (3.1 KG)

COLORATION

THERE ARE TWO COLOR VARIETIES OF THE ARCTIC FOX. THE MOST COMMON AND WIDESPREAD IN THE FAR NORTH IS CREAMY WHITE IN WINTER, MOLTING IN PATCHES TO A SUMMER COAT OF GRAY BROWN ABOVE AND CREAM BELOW, WITH WHITE EYEBROWS AND EAR LININGS. THE LESS COMMON BLUE FORM IS ACTUALLY DEEP BROWN WITH A METALLIC BLUE-GRAY SHEEN IN WINTER, MOLTING TO BROWN IN SUMMER

FEATURES

EXTREMELY THICK, LUXURIANT WINTER COAT

BUSHY TAIL

SLIM LEGS

SHORT MUZZLE, COMPARED WITH OTHER FOXES

COMPARATIVELY SHORT, ROUNDED EARS

THE TAIL

is long and bushy, and the fox uses it like a fur stole to keep its face warm when it curls up to sleep on the ice. Tail gestures help foxes communicate when they are in sight of each other.

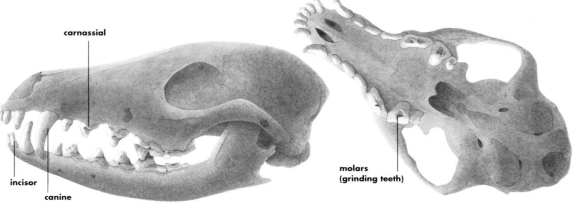

A typical fox has a long jaw with a varied array of teeth, including large, bladelike carnassials toward the back of the jaw; these act against each other like scissors to shear through skin, sinew, and flesh. The sideways movement of the jaw is restricted to keep these scissor blades in alignment, so the fox cannot grind its food like a dedicated plant-eater.

carnassial

incisor

canine

molars
(grinding teeth)

Main illustration Steve Kingston

LIVING ON THEIR WITS

ALTHOUGH FOXES ARE NOMINALLY CARNIVORES, MOST WILL EAT A SURPRISING VARIETY OF FOODS. THIS WILLINGNESS TO EXPERIMENT IS A THREAD THAT RUNS THROUGHOUT THEIR BEHAVIOR

Oblivious to the flies swarming around its head, a brown-coated arctic fox roots through the jetsam dumped high on an Icelandic beach by an Atlantic storm. Barely visible against the dark sand in the bleak northern twilight, it tugs at a bunch of feathers and hauls out the remains of a long-dead herring gull, its once-bright plumage now matted with oil and filth. Undeterred, the fox tears into the carcass, ripping the skin and crunching through flesh and bone with the big "scissor" teeth at the side of its mouth. It eats fast, gulping down the rancid meat in chunks, then picks up the remains and trots away up the beach to cache them well above the shoreline.

Rotting seagull may not be its preferred food, but the arctic fox is not fussy. On Iceland, where there are no native rodents such as lemmings or voles to tempt the palate, beachcombing is a way of life for many of the local foxes. Seabirds, clams, dead fish, and seal carcasses are all welcome additions to the menu, and a fox will even snap up the beach flies if they are all the shoreline has to offer. An arctic fox is hardly equipped for efficient flycatching—but then it is not highly adapted to eat anything in particular: It has retained the flexibility to eat virtually anything that offers a reasonable level of nutrition. This rules out leaves and grass, for as a normal carnivore the fox lacks the complex digestive system necessary to deal with bulky, fibrous material; but it will sample anything else from a bilberry to a stranded whale.

TUNDRA LIFE

This opportunism is the key to the arctic fox's success on Iceland. The foxes time their visits to the beach to coincide with the ebb of the tide. They never know what they will find on the shoreline, but their willingness to eat whatever there is can be measured by their breeding performance, which remains stable year after year. By contrast, arctic foxes living on the Siberian tundra rely heavily on lemmings for prey; and since lemming populations are notoriously volatile, the foxes have to cope with periodic famines. The shortage of their main food affects their breeding performance, but once again a type of opportunism ensures that there is no lasting damage. In good "lemming years" the foxes take

KEY FACTS

- Although the arctic fox only starts shivering at –94°F (–70°C), the fennec fox begins to shiver as soon as desert temperatures drop below 68°F (20°C).

- In 1868 a scientist described the South American foxes as "fox-tailed wolves"—an eccentric description that has now been vindicated by analysis of blood proteins.

- The camouflage of the arctic fox has evolved as a defense against birds of prey such as eagles, which hunt mainly by sight. A larger carnivore such as a wolverine could easily sniff out an arctic fox, however well disguised.

- Bat-eared foxes are very social animals—for foxes—and may live in family groups of up to twelve adults.

- In South America the native foxes are called *zorros*, which is simply Spanish for *fox*. The word is sometimes used to distinguish these animals from the more familiar vulpine foxes.

Learning can be fun. Arctic fox cubs brush up on their hunting skills while at play (below).

Kathy Bushue/Tony Stone Images

advantage of the wealth of prey to breed at a prodigious rate, and this effectively offsets the breeding failures of the bad years.

In the harsh, unstable conditions of the far north, opportunism may be essential for survival, but foxes throughout the world display the same flexibility. In South America a prowling crab-eating fox will certainly snap up a land crab if it finds one, but it may also raid a chicken run, dig up a nest of turtle eggs, or steal a bunch of bananas. Its habits tend to change with the seasons, but they cannot be predicted: The fox switches from one food source to another to take advantage of easy pickings, and near the equator it even breeds at random times of the year in response to periods of good living.

The willingness of foxes to exploit temporary situations is fundamental to their behavior. Within any species individual foxes can be found acting in very different ways, and although the members of a local population generally share the same way of life, each fox tends to have its own distinct approach to each challenge. This is partly because of their inherently predatory nature. Hunters live on their wits, and thus develop an acute intelligence. Such intelligence tends to displace instinct as a controlling factor on behavior, and the less instinctively animals behave, the less predictable they are. Conversely, if unpredictability is any measure of intelligence, foxes are very smart indeed. ∎

The snowy fur of the arctic fox is probably the most efficient thermal "jacket" of any land mammal.

Odd Ivar Rudd/Tony Stone Images

HABITATS

The savannas of tropical Africa have been called
the greatest wildlife spectacle on earth. Vast
herds of grazing animals—zebras, antelopes,
gazelles—wander the plains pursued by lions, cheetahs, and wild dogs. In some areas the grazers drift
like waves across the seas of grass: Plains zebras
take the long, coarse stems, while blue wildebeest
follow behind to tear at the shorter, juicier foliage
beneath; then Thomson's gazelles nibble the
remains almost to the ground before moving on.

Once the gazelles have fed there is little left for
grazing mammals, but plenty for the smaller creatures. The tender shoots sprouting from the mown
sward are relished by tiny harvester termites, grass-
eating insects that swarm in vast numbers. The big
herbivores scatter plenty of dung, which attracts an
army of creatures such as dung beetles; these and
the termites are an abundant source of food for any
animal that can eat them—such as the bat-eared fox.

Martin Wendler/NHPA

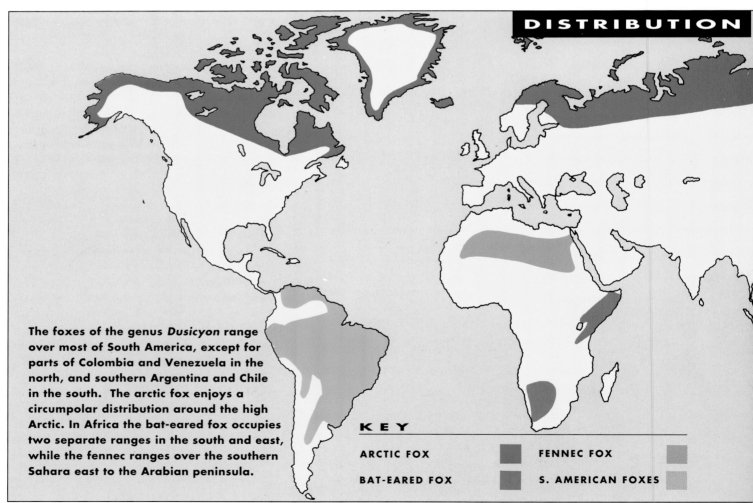

DISTRIBUTION

The foxes of the genus *Dusicyon* range
over most of South America, except for
parts of Colombia and Venezuela in the
north, and southern Argentina and Chile
in the south. The arctic fox enjoys a
circumpolar distribution around the high
Arctic. In Africa the bat-eared fox occupies
two separate ranges in the south and east,
while the fennec ranges over the southern
Sahara east to the Arabian peninsula.

KEY

ARCTIC FOX   FENNEC FOX

BAT-EARED FOX   S. AMERICAN FOXES

The crab-eating fox (left) is widespread through-out the woodlands of northern South America.

Uniquely among foxes, the habitat of this insect-eating specialist is defined by its diet, so it dwells only on the termite-ridden grasslands. At one time it roamed all over the African plains from Somalia to the Cape, but climatic changes and human pressures have created two separate populations: one in east Africa and one in the south. Within these areas the bat-eared fox is common and widespread, just like its prey, and although its neighbors include other termite-eaters, such as the aardwolf, it never has to compete for its niche with other foxes.

The seven or so South American fox species all have a typically broad diet, so their habitats are broader in scope. They are, however, constrained by competition between species. The colpeo fox, for example, is found along the Pacific coast, where its range overlaps with that of the Argentine gray fox. In the north of this overlap zone, the two species are so similar that they would certainly compete for resources—except that the colpeo has become

Eyal Bartou/Oxford Scientific Films

ISLAND BLUES

Most arctic foxes turn white in winter, and over most of the fox's vast continental range less than one percent are the blue form. This is probably because blue-brown foxes are conspicuous in snowbound winter landscapes, making stealthy hunting more difficult and increasing their vulnerability to eagles and other predators. As a result the blue strain tends not to establish where winter snow cover is normal.

In coastal areas, however, the snow cover is patchy. In such conditions white foxes are at a disadvantage compared to the blue form, so blues are more common. They are particularly numerous on islands, which have extensive coastlines. The smaller the island, the more coastline relative to the snowbound interior, and the more blues there are. So on Iceland roughly two-thirds of the foxes are blues, and on the Icelandic coast, at any rate, a white arctic fox is a rare sight. Nevertheless, Iceland is still home to both color forms, and in such regions where they coincide, white foxes readily mate with blue foxes and seem unaware of any difference, either in their mates or in the resulting cubs.

A desert foxhole on the Sinai plains gives shelter to its creator—the tiny fennec fox.

adapted to the conditions found at higher altitudes in the Andes. This allows it to exploit the "fox niche" on the alpine slopes while its sister species exploits the same niche in the foothills.

In the deserts of Arabia the little fennec fox manages to coexist with the similar Blanford's fox on the same principle. The fennec can thrive on sand dunes: It has furred soles that provide insulation and grip on the hot, unstable sand and a variety of adaptations for survival in the bone-dry climate. Its huge ears are laced with blood vessels so that they can dissipate heat, and if the air temperature soars above the fox's normal body temperature of 100.8°F (38.2°C), the fennec can allow itself to heat up to 105.6°F (40.9°C) without suffering heatstroke. This delays the onset of heavy panting. When it pants it curls its tongue to conserve saliva, and it rarely has to drink. It can obtain all the water it needs from its prey, provided it lies low during the heat of the day.

These traits are impressive, but not unique. Many of the fennec's adaptations are shared by Blanford's fox, among others; but where the two species occur in the same region, direct competition is prevented by specific adaptations to different types of terrain. Where the fennec has furred feet for hunting over shifting sands, Blanford's fox has naked foot pads to provide adhesion for hunting over cliffs and crags. Because of this the two rarely come into conflict over the same food resources.

The fennec's smaller size may also reduce conflict with its near relatives, since it is satisfied with smaller prey. Back in South America, the colpeo fox and the Argentine gray fox are the same size where their habitats are separated by altitude, but in parts of Chile where the mountains are lower the two may share terrain. Here, natural selection has favored a smaller race of the Argentine gray fox and a larger race of the colpeo. The size difference allows them to exploit different prey and thereby to coexist.

Up in the far north the arctic fox crosses paths with the larger red fox in many areas—often to its disadvantage, as red foxes may kill arctic foxes that compete for the same food resources. However, the arctic fox can live much farther north than its red cousin, owing partly to its smaller size, which allows it to thrive on the slim pickings to be had during the long northern winter. The Arctic summer lasts little more than two months, and much of the wildlife moves south for winter. Some arctic foxes do likewise, but many stay on to hunt lemmings and other small creatures in their runs under the snow.

Small size has its drawbacks, however, particularly in cold habitats. A smaller animal has a larger surface area relative to its mass, and this increases its tendency to lose heat. To counter this the arctic fox has developed the most luxuriant fur of any

mammal, proof against almost anything the polar climate can throw at it. Roughly 70 percent of its winter coat consists of fleecy underfur, compared to 20 percent in the red fox, and this insulates the animal so effectively that it begins to shiver only if the temperature drops below –94°F (–70°C). This allows it to venture farther north than any other canid: It has been recorded breeding on the sea ice north of Greenland at a latitude of 88 degrees north—a mere two degrees from the North Pole, and a long way from the savannas of tropical Africa. ■

FOCUS ON

ARCTIC SHORES

In the brief Arctic summer, the northern coasts of European Russia are transformed into immense nurseries as the cliffs above the cold gray waters of the Arctic Ocean become occupied by vast colonies of breeding seabirds. Jostling for space on narrow ledges, rows of guillemots, razorbills, and kittiwakes incubate their eggs and rear their chicks, commuting between the cliffs and the rich, teeming ocean with small fish to stuff into gaping bills.

The prime breeding sites are in the middle of the colony, safe from the attacks of black-backed gulls, skuas, and arctic foxes. The foxes are fearless in their attempts to raid the cliffside nests, but their big chance comes when the fledglings leave the nest. Not only must the young birds run the gauntlet of predators, they also have to avoid crash-diving into the rocks on their first flight. Encouraged by the calls of the parent birds bobbing on the waves, the young hopefuls dive from their ledges, furiously flapping their tiny wings. Most of them make it to the sea, but some misjudge the attempt or are blown onto the beach, into the jaws of waiting foxes. Significantly, arctic foxes living near these great seabird colonies have a far more stable breeding record than their inland counterparts, which do not have access to such a seasonal feast.

Norbert Rosing/Oxford Scientific Films

TEMPERATURE AND RAINFALL

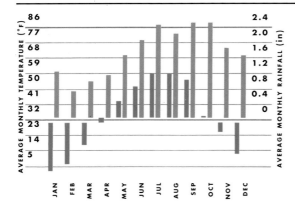

■ TEMPERATURE

■ RAINFALL

The figures here relate to Archangel, on the White Sea. Russia's northern coasts straddle the Arctic Circle and are out of reach of the Gulf Stream. Here the winters are bitterly cold. The summers are very wet, with tolerably mild temperatures.

NEIGHBORS

Despite the harshness of its climate, the Arctic teems with wildlife. This is due mainly to the icy waters, which have a high oxygen content. Nevertheless, life is rarely easy for denizens of the north.

IVORY GULL

This pure-white gull lives around the Arctic ice floes, scavenging the dung and kills of polar bears.

POLAR BEAR

The polar bear's luxuriant coat consists of hollow, colorless hairs that both insulate and solar heat the skin.

Neighbor illustrations Elisabeth Smith, Peter Bull, Ruth Grewcock, Joanne Cowne, Jim Higgins/Wildlife Art Agency

RUSSIA'S SHORES

Away from the huge port of Archangel, the Russian shores west of the Urals are desolate; they are also bitterly cold. Their proximity to warmer regions of Europe, notably Scandinavia, has no bearing on the localized climate that grips the aptly named White Sea, which, in severe winters, may freeze over entirely.

Barents Sea

FINLAND

White Sea

● ARCHANGEL

RUSSIA

GYRFALCON

The largest of all falcons, the gyrfalcon swoops on anything from ptarmigans to rabbits or weasels.

NORWAY LEMMING

A mouselike rodent, the lemming is one of the most important elements in the northern food chain.

PUFFIN

The brightly billed puffin nests in clifftop burrows and dives for fish in coastal water.

ERMINE

In the northern reaches of its wide range, the stoat, or ermine, grows a luxuriant white coat in winter.

EIDER

Great "rafts" of these hardy sea ducks gather in the icy, choppy waters off northern shores.

HUNTING

Foxes, it could be said, are among the impulse buyers of the animal world. Other carnivores often seem to hunt with the aid of a mental shopping list: A weasel, for example, will put its head into every crevice to sniff for rodents, while a pack of wild dogs may deliberately set out to hunt zebra and ignore easier targets nearby. But a typical fox is no specialist feeder with clear ideas about the food it will eat. It can be tempted by anything that it deems edible: animal or vegetable, alive or dead.

Yet while most foxes have avoided specializing in particular hunting methods, they are no slouches at the trade. They may lack the sheer killing power that regularly enables more dedicated predators to overwhelm animals larger than themselves, but their efficiency as hunters of small game makes such risky exploits unnecessary. With a few exceptions, foxes of all kinds are flourishing in the widest possible variety of circumstances.

SUMMER GLUT

The arctic fox exploits rich summer resources by killing as much prey as it can and hiding the surplus to eat in leaner months (below).

EGG THIEF

Despite its name, the crab-eating fox eats more or less anything it can find, including turtle eggs (below).

Illustration Mark Stewart/Wildlife Art Agency

Stan Osolinski/Oxford Scientific Films

A bat-eared fox temporarily forsakes its staple diet of insects and successfully waylays a snake.

In the baked heart of the Sahara, for example, the delicate fennec preys mainly on desert rodents such as gerbils—wary, fast-moving animals—as well as lizards, insects, and small birds. It normally spends the day keeping cool in a hollow and emerges to hunt in the cool dusk and dawn. Like all foxes it has excellent night vision; but as it zigzags across the cooling dunes in the tropical twilight, it relies on its big ears to register the slightest rustle or squeak of potential prey. Once alerted, it freezes on the spot and swivels its head to pinpoint the source of the sound, then stalks closer. Once within range it leaps and pounces down with its forefeet to pin the victim to the ground before killing it.

This leaping pounce is a typical fox maneuver. An arctic fox will use the same technique to catch a lemming on the northern tundra, carefully tracking its progress along its run beneath the snow before leaping high to punch down through the icy crust and flatten its target. On open ground the same tactic serves to counter the instinctive tendency of a small rodent to leap up to avoid danger.

Different types of prey demand different means of attack, however, and in South America a colpeo fox may snatch itself a rabbit simply by hurtling toward a feeding group at full speed and grabbing the nearest one before it gets the chance to bolt. The little-known Azara's fox of southeastern South America also preys regularly on rabbits, but many of the South American foxes are smaller and prefer

less powerful quarry. For example, rabbits account for only 3 percent of the diet of the lightweight Argentine gray fox, and when the species was introduced to Tierra del Fuego in the late 1940s in a poorly researched effort to control the multiplying rabbit population, the foxes ignored the rabbits and turned on the native ruddy-headed geese instead.

Geese are no easy prey themselves, though. On Wrangel Island, off the Arctic coast of Siberia, arctic foxes breed alongside snow geese in summer. In years when lemmings are numerous, the foxes usually give the geese a wide berth; but if the lemming population crashes—as it tends to do every four years—the foxes have to forage elsewhere. The snow goose colony is a tempting proposition, and foxes spend a lot of time trying to sneak close enough to make off with the eggs and goslings. Particularly bold individuals may also attack the incubating birds, but it is a hazardous business. An arctic fox is no match for a healthy adult snow goose, and the prowling foxes are generally driven away, pecked and bruised by the powerful wings of the enraged parents.

LEMMING CYCLES

Arctic foxes are among the most opportunistic of the foxes; the instability of their food resources leaves them little option. The lemming crash every four

HANGER-ON

Come winter, when other prey is scarce, many arctic foxes resort to scavenging from the kills of polar bears—such as this seal (below left).

DESERT HUNTER

Though it forages more often in the cool of the Sahara night, the fennec may emerge by day to exploit cold-blooded prey (below).

A VINTAGE YEAR!

Foxy by nature if not strictly by name, a gray zorro (below) shows typical cunning in stealing grapes from a Chilean vineyard.

years is just one aspect of the cyclic "boom and bust" ecology of the far north, in which periods of plenty are interspersed with periods of near famine. On the Arctic coasts and islands, for example, the local foxes are spoiled with choices in the summer when the seabirds are nesting, but in winter the breeding colonies are deserted and the foxes have to fall back on scavenging, both along the shores and out on the sea ice. Many foxes travel great distances in search of food in the lean months, and most are nomadic for much of the year. They often trail after polar bears, hoping to inherit the remains of seal kills; polar bears frequently leave significant remains of their seal victims, so a patient fox stands to gain a lot. Some arctic foxes may spend the whole winter scavenging polar bear kills on the sea ice, but they have to be careful: Polar bears have been known to kill foxes that stray too close.

Where fresh carrion is not available, arctic foxes are not averse to eating long-dead meat. Their cold habitat helps here: On one occasion at least 40 arctic foxes were seen feeding together on a deep-frozen walrus carcass, having dug and gnawed their way through some 2 ft (60 cm) of ice to reach it. Like nearly all foxes, they will also cache food against hard times. In late spring lemmings are often flushed out of their burrows by meltwater and are easy to catch; the foxes often react by killing more than they need and storing the surplus. The leanest time comes before this, however, in early

in SIGHT

TOUGH NEIGHBORS

Arctic foxes are resourceful predators, but they do not always get their own way. Many birds, in particular, have evolved defense strategies, of which the most remarkable example is probably that of red-breasted geese.

These handsome birds nearly always nest in colonies of up to six pairs, close by the nest of a powerful raptor such as a peregrine falcon. Since peregrines feed mainly on birds, this might seem foolhardy; but apparently the hawks never harm the redbreasts—possibly because they hunt elsewhere. In any event the risk pays off, since the nesting peregrines make superb guards. A fox might well try its luck with a goose, but it is no match for a peregrine, which is capable of killing it outright. After a couple of attempts the foxes stay away, leaving the birds to breed in peace.

Illustration Robin Budden/Wildlife Art Agency

BAT-EARED FOXES
listen at a termite mound. On the savanna, the total weight of resident termites may be more than double that of hoofed mammals in a single area, providing a vast food resource for foxes.

Cruising for carrion: An Argentine gray fox makes a meal of a washed-up penguin carcass.

Jen & Des Bartlett/Bruce Coleman Ltd.

spring, and the foxes prepare early by building up food caches several months beforehand.

In the far south, some South American species experience similar winter food shortages and the Argentine gray fox is often badly hit by heavy snow-fall in chilly Patagonia, with many individuals starving to death. By comparison, conditions in the tropics are relatively stable, enabling the bat-eared fox of the African savannas to feed on termites and other insects all year-round. Like the fennec, it relies heavily on the supersensitivity of its enormous ears to locate its prey; indeed, its hearing is so acute that it can detect the faint sound of the insects moving through soil tunnels as they commute between their underground nests and their feeding areas. Having pinpointed the sound, the fox digs down and laps up as many insects as possible before they scatter. It uses a similar technique to locate dung beetle larvae, which feed within balls of dung buried by the adults. The sound of the larva gnawing at its food store beneath the ground attracts the fox, which then digs it out and devours it. ∎

MUTE BUTTON

Having picked up the faint scrabbling of dung beetles in the soil, a bat-eared fox digs deep and snaps them up (above).

695

TERRITORY

Most foxes stay within a well-defined area, which enables them to memorize food sources, danger zones, and refuges from the weather or enemies. It may also give the resident a partial monopoly over its food supply, provided the area can be defended from neighboring foxes. Effective defense of any territory depends upon its size, however, and this in turn depends upon the richness of the habitat.

In tropical America, for example, the wealth of food available allows the crab-eating fox to spend most of its life foraging over a small home range. In the high Arctic, by contrast, food is so scarce for much of the year that many arctic foxes make huge seasonal treks over the tundra and sea ice, searching for carrion, scraps, and live prey. In one case a tagged fox was recovered over 5,600 miles (9,000 km) from its birthplace. In milder conditions arctic foxes may forage over regular home ranges; but these can still be vast, and if need be, can extend to 15,000 acres (6,000 hectares) on the northern tundra.

Such vast areas cannot be defended as exclusive property, but roaming foxes of all species regularly mark the terrain with urine, scats, and secretions from their anal musk glands. Such scent marks are interesting both to "resident" foxes and others, enabling these solitary animals to communicate.

In coastal regions the wealth of food cast up on the shoreline allows beachcombing arctic foxes to restrict their foraging to smaller ranges than their tundra cousins. In one Icelandic study, coastal foxes lived in territories each extending some 3–7.5 miles (5–12 km) along the shore. Each coastal territory was occupied by three foxes: a mature

Jeff Foott/Okapia/Oxford Scientific Films

pair and a young adult female probably born the previous season. Although most foxes hunt alone, studies show that many species share their feeding ranges. In the Icelandic study, breeding pairs were probably willing to share because the adult daughter helped rear the next cubs.

In Africa similar factors enable bat-eared foxes to share territories. Since their insect prey is abundant on the savanna, these foxes hold territories of

The Argentine gray fox (above) may share its South American range with the colpeo fox.

BEACH PARTY

The size of an arctic fox range and the extent to which it is shared depend partly on the tides that dump food debris on the shore (below).

only 0.2–1.1 sq mi (0.5–2.9 sq km), but each territory includes several termite runs. When a fox breaks into a termite run it may be faced with more insects than it can eat in the short time before they scatter, so there is every incentive for two or three foxes to feed together. Accordingly bat-eared foxes generally live in extended family groups of three or more adults, plus growing cubs. This has an extra advantage, for they are vulnerable to larger predators such as big cats, and there is safety in numbers. ■

ⓘⓝSIGHT

ANCESTRAL HOMES

Most foxes make their dens in rock crevices or dig inconspicuous burrows in soft soil, but such easy options are rarely available to the arctic fox. On the bleak, open Arctic tundra, rocky den sites can be scarce; and since the soil is permanently frozen just below the surface, digging is normally impossible and usually rather debilitating in terms of energy expenditure. This puts a high premium on good den sites, and foxes that find a suitable raised area with dry, friable soil will use the same site for generation after generation, even for several centuries.

These ancestral dens often develop into prominent features of the tundra terrain. Food remains and droppings scattered around the many entrances increase the fertility of the soil, so the site is gradually covered with luxuriant plant growth that contrasts with the pinched vegetation of the surrounding tundra. Since such dens are usually sited on higher ground to prevent flooding, the result is a den that looks more like a castle—a fitting home for these Arctic marauders.

Chris Shields/Wildlife Art Agency.

REPRODUCTION

Breeding foxes typically form stable pairs, unlike most mammals, and the male stays near his mate throughout the gestation, suckling, and weaning periods. He keeps her supplied with food while she is confined to the den and brings solid food to the cubs when they are ready to eat it. Eventually both parents share the job of bringing food until the cubs are ready to venture out and forage with them. Ultimately the family may break up as the young animals mature and disperse, but in some species young adults stay within their parents' territory for another year or two.

Most South American foxes seem to stick fairly close to this pattern. The female colpeo fox, for example, mates between August and October and, after a gestation of two months, gives birth to an average of five cubs. The cubs are born in a secure nursery den hidden among vegetation or concealed beneath rocks, since they are virtually helpless during the first two weeks and at risk from predators and the elements. Newborn cubs cannot regulate their body temperatures well, so they must huddle together to stay warm; in many habitats the shelter of a snug den is vital to their survival.

The female stays with her cubs constantly for the first few days, while the male supplies her with food—both for her own maintenance and to keep up her milk supply. The responsibility of feeding his mate and cubs tends to discourage polygamy on the part of the male, since if he sires another family he has to split his time between them and collect twice as much food. Such circumstances may arise with bat-eared foxes, but there is no evidence that males ever abandon females, leaving them to raise cubs on their own. Male foxes try to secure the success of their dynasty by maximizing the survival rate of their young, rather than generating as many offspring as possible by mating promiscuously.

HELPERS

Child care is such a high priority among foxes that many species employ other adults to help at the den. These are typically the young from previous seasons who have stayed with their parents instead of dispersing. Among lupine canids the young of both sexes may take this option, forming the basis of the pack. Possibly because they share lupine origins, the South American foxes, such as the crab-eating fox,

An Argentine gray fox suckles her young (below). She can also rely on help from nonbreeding females.

Gunter Ziesler/Bruce Coleman Ltd.

BLUES AND WHITES

Despite the comparative rarity of blue arctic foxes worldwide, the blue gene that creates them is actually dominant while the white gene is recessive. This means that if a purebred blue fox, with two blue genes, mates with a white fox with two white genes, their hybrid cubs will all be blue. Genetically, however, each of these blue hybrids carries one blue and one white gene, and if such a cub matures and mates with a white fox, some of their cubs may inherit two white genes while others get one blue and one white. The result is a mixed litter, with some white and some blue. Even more oddly, if two blue hybrids mate they may produce white cubs. Such things happen regularly, for there is no color prejudice among arctic foxes.

CAUTIOUS PROVIDER

The male fennec fox brings food to his mate while she is nursing. She protects her litter fiercely, so he carefully drops it at the den entrance.

Illustrations Carol Roberts

FROM BIRTH TO DEATH

ARCTIC FOX	
GESTATION: 53 DAYS	**WEIGHT AT BIRTH:** 2 OZ (56 G)
LITTER SIZE: UP TO 19, AVERAGE 7	**EYES OPEN:** 2 WEEKS
BREEDING: MATES IN APRIL, GIVES	**WEANING:** 6 WEEKS
BIRTH IN JUNE; THEN MAY MATE	**INDEPENDENCE:** 6 MONTHS
AGAIN	**SEXUAL MATURITY:** 10 MONTHS
	LONGEVITY: UP TO 10 YEARS

do the same. Young crab-eating foxes may leave home and then return to help with the new brood. Among vulpines the young males nearly always leave for good, and only the daughters remain behind. The "helpers" share the task of feeding the young cubs and may guard them at the den while the parents are out hunting.

For most species the pattern remains stable year after year, but the fennec and the arctic fox have adapted to their tough environments by evolving fail-safe breeding strategies. Unusually for a wild canid, the fennec can produce two litters in a single season. If the first litter of between two and five cubs is lost, the female may mate again and give birth to a second litter a few months later.

The arctic fox may also breed twice in one season, but this is not just a response to a lost litter. The tundra lemming supply lurches from over-load to scarcity over a four-year cycle as the rodents breed rapidly, eat out their food resources, die off in droves, and then start breeding rapidly again to exploit new vegetation. The foxes respond by breeding prolifically in the good years, raising one or two litters of 11 cubs or more, to make up for the famine years when they do not breed at all; the largest arctic fox litter ever recorded was 19 cubs.

On the continental tundra where the foxes rely heavily on lemmings, these breeding peaks and troughs tend to follow those of the lemmings, so both animals display four-year cycles of abundance and scarcity. Near the coasts, however, where arctic foxes enjoy a more regular food supply of seabirds and carrion, the breeding pattern is more stable and huge litters are rare. ■

SURVIVAL TECHNIQUES

Like most foxes, fennecs depend on lightning-fast reactions when pouncing on prey. Cubs practice these and other skills in play.

FOXY FORTUNES

ALTHOUGH FOXES HAVE BEEN PERSECUTED FOR CENTURIES, THEY HAVE A NATURAL ABILITY TO RECOVER FROM SETBACKS. THE MAIN THREAT TO THEIR SURVIVAL TODAY IS THE ALTERATION OF THEIR WILD HABITATS

Foxes are among the most resilient of wild mammals. Not only are they adaptable creatures, individually well equipped to change their behavior to suit altered circumstances, but their populations are capable of recovering from catastrophes that might be fatal to other species.

This capacity for bouncing back from the edge of oblivion is particularly well developed in the arctic fox, which has evolved to survive one of the harshest environments on earth. In some years prey famines on the bleak winter tundra have wiped out over three-quarters of a local fox population, but by breeding at record levels the survivors can make up the numbers in a matter of months. Because of this resilience, trapping and shooting make little long-term difference to most arctic fox populations. This is just as well, because, like many other foxes worldwide, they have been relentlessly persecuted by humans.

One of the main reasons for this is their incomparable fur coat. An arctic fox in its winter coat has a fleecy pelt that is many times warmer than that of any other fur-bearing animal, and its market value is correspondingly high. The blue form is more valuable than the white; and since blue arctic foxes are most numerous in accessible coastal areas and islands, they are particularly vulnerable. Arctic foxes are heavily hunted in Iceland, partly for their fur and partly because they are accused of killing lambs and are therefore regarded as vermin. The Icelandic government actually spends some $200,000 a year on a control program, using professional hunters who shoot about 900 foxes annually—roughly half the adult fox population of the island—plus some 1,300 cubs. Despite this the foxes still flourish and are even increasing in some areas. A species that has developed the ability to withstand the polar winter has not been discouraged by a few people with rifles.

Farther north there is no farming lobby, since farming is next to impossible on the tundra, so the arctic fox is killed solely for its fur. Here the annual fox kill has dwindled in recent years, largely because it is easier to breed the animals in captivity than to hunt or trap them in the northern winter. In Scandinavia such fur farming has become a major industry, and of the 3.3 million fox pelts traded in 1988–89, for example, 2.6 million came from fur farms in Scandinavia. The ready availability of captive-bred pelts has made wild-trapping a much less viable proposition, and in

John Daniels/Ardea

Equipped for the coldest weather on Earth, the arctic fox is more than a match for humans (above).

*This map shows the current distribution of
the fennec fox.*

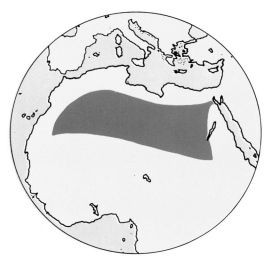

■ **FENNEC FOX DISTRIBUTION**

**Despite its ability to penetrate the
scorched dunes and plains of the Sahara,
the fennec is under heavy pressure. In
parts of northern Africa it is intensively
hunted, and its populations have been
fragmented in the more populated regions
of the Arabian peninsula. It was reported
some years ago to survive in Kuwait, but
the Gulf War temporarily created problems
for this isolated population.**

North America the number of wild arctic foxes
trapped annually has fallen from some 70,000 in the
1930s to less than 20,000.

The fox still faces problems, however, on islands
such as Wrangel, off the Siberian coast, which hosts
both foxes and snow geese. The two species once
lived in harmony, since the foxes generally only
picked off the weaker geese, which were less likely
to produce healthy young. When humans arrived in
1926 they decimated the goose colonies and, until
very recently, shot the foxes that raided the goose
nests. In the late 1980s it was suggested that
Nature's original way had been the best; the shooting was banned and the geese duly recovered.

The arctic fox might be a born survivor, but
other species may be less able to sustain such hunting pressures. In South America the Argentine gray

*The fennec is under increasing pressure from
huntsmen in its remote desert homeland.*

701

OUT OF ACTION

INSIDIOUS INSECTICIDES

In the African tropics cattle and other domestic animals are plagued by parasitic insects that bore into their skin and lay eggs. These hatch into larvae that feed on the tissues of the animal, weakening it and rendering it extremely vulnerable to infection. In the past the local herdsmen made the best of this or used breeds with some resistance to the worst effects of such infestation, but today they have another option: chemical insecticides.

The insecticides permeate the animal's system and kill off any parasites that may have taken up residence. But they may also move right through its digestive tract to be eventually expelled in its dung—and this creates a serious problem. On the savannas the main recyclers of dung are insects, including dung beetles, and the poisons kill them just as surely as they kill the internal parasites. Since dung beetles are among those insects eaten by bat-eared foxes, the adoption of such pest control methods could eventually destroy a major element of their food supply and drive them off the broad, fertile grasslands they have occupied for five million years or more.

Jen & Des Bartlett/Survival Anglia

fox has been very heavily trapped for its fur, with the trade peaking at over a million pelts per year in the early 1980s. Most of these came from Argentina, but pelts were also coming out of Chile, where the species is scarce and nominally under state protection. Currently there is little data on how the gray fox is coping with this, although some populations under observation seem to be thriving. Other South American foxes have definitely suffered: Azara's fox, a native of central South America east of the Andes, has declined in several parts of its range as a result of hunting, trapping, and poisoning, and several other species may be under threat, both from hunting and habitat destruction.

FLOURISHING IN AFRICA

In Africa the fennec fox has declined in some parts of its range owing to hunting, but its desert habitat is almost immune to further degradation by man. On the savannas the bat-eared fox might be vulnerable, and it is probable that its division into two large populations has been partly caused by hunting, but the expansion of man's influence on the African

The Argentine gray fox is probably the most threatened fox species in South America.

grasslands may actually help the species rather than discourage it. Bat-eared foxes flourish in areas where the grass is nibbled down by large grazing animals, and they are not particular about the nature of the grazers. Cattle do the job for them as efficiently as zebra and wildebeest, and as long as the ranchers do not try to curb the insect populations on the savannas, the bat-eared foxes will flourish regardless. ∎

FOXES IN DANGER

THE CHART BELOW SHOWS HOW, IN 1994, THE INTERNATIONAL UNION FOR THE CONSERVATION OF NATURE (IUCN) CLASSIFIED THE CONSERVATION STATUS OF FOXES (EXCLUDING THE GENUS *VULPES*) THAT ARE KNOWN OR SUSPECTED TO BE UNDER THREAT.

ARGENTINE GRAY FOX	VULNERABLE
SECHURAN FOX	INSUFFICIENTLY KNOWN
HOARY FOX	INSUFFICIENTLY KNOWN
SMALL-EARED DOG	INSUFFICIENTLY KNOWN
FENNEC FOX	INSUFFICIENTLY KNOWN

VULNERABLE MEANS THAT THE SPECIES IS LIKELY TO DECLINE AND BECOME SERIOUSLY ENDANGERED IF NOTHING IS DONE TO IMPROVE ITS SITUATION. *INSUFFICIENTLY KNOWN* MEANS THAT THE SPECIES IS SUSPECTED TO BE THREATENED, BUT THERE IS NOT ENOUGH INFORMATION TO BE SURE.

INTO THE FUTURE

Conservationists have an information problem: Of the five species of nonvulpine foxes listed by the IUCN, four are "insufficiently known" for scientists to come to any useful conclusions about the threats they face. This means that, apart from issuing vague warnings against hunting and habitat destruction, they can offer no structured formulas for their survival.

For example, the small-eared dog of the Amazon basin has proved so elusive that a zoologist who has worked in the region for 20 years has never seen one. Other South American foxes are almost as mysterious. Of the six surviving species of the South American foxes, only three have been studied in any detail, and the information available on the others amounts to little more than basic descriptions and rough distribution data. So if one of these obscure foxes starts to decline seriously, no one will know

PREDICTION

HOPE FOR RABIES

The threat of rabies—which is a much greater threat to wild foxes than it is to domestic dogs and people—may soon be eradicated through inoculation of wild populations using bait laced with rabies vaccine.

until the process is well advanced—and it may be impossible to isolate the reasons for the problem.

The good news is that this ignorance stems from a lack of observation, which in turn indicates a scarcity of observers. Many South American foxes live in remote regions where humans are few, and this can only be to their advantage. The same can be said of the fennec and the arctic fox, whose adaptations to extreme climates enable them to live in conditions that deter human settlement.

Disease, however, is a serious threat to all wild canids. Dogs and foxes are susceptible to a range of infections including mange, distemper, rabies, and a variety of obscure viruses. Small, dense populations are highly vulnerable, and as wild animals become increasingly confined to isolated refuges—whether "protected" or otherwise—by human activity, the danger of disease increases. Luckily, most foxes are adaptable enough to avoid being confined to such potential death traps, so their prospects for the future are comparatively bright. ∎

LOSING CONTROL

In the Russian and Siberian Arctic, wildlife has enjoyed a measure of protection over the past few decades thanks to conservation laws and the establishment of nature preserves on the Kola Peninsula, the Taimyr Peninsula, and Wrangel Island. Extensive studies of the wildlife in these preserves have yielded a wealth of information on the behavior and ecology of native animals, including the arctic fox, and several threatened species have been rescued from the edge of extinction. But all this may change.

The breakup of the former Soviet Union has created a new climate of uncontrolled, largely illegal private enterprise that encourages local entrepreneurs to exploit the landscape for their own profit. Without the backing of a strong central government, the conservation authorities are powerless to prevent this, and the wildlife of several preserves is now being exploited on a large scale. Animals such as the arctic fox, which has a valuable pelt, make tempting targets for poachers, and isolated populations such as that on Wrangel Island could easily be wiped out. To make matters worse, there are other, less direct threats: One race of the arctic fox, restricted to Mednij Island off the coast of northeastern Siberia, has been reduced to near-extinction by an epidemic of mange introduced by domestic dogs.

Illustration Kim Thompson

Vulpine Foxes

Foxes belong to the mammal order Carnivora and the dog family, Canidae. Other canids include:

WOLVES

JACKALS

COYOTE

DINGO

MANED WOLF

BUSH DOG

RACCOON DOG

Darrell Gulin/Tony Stone Worldwide

CLASSIFICATION

There are two main types of foxes: the vulpines, mostly classified in the genus Vulpes, and the more lupine (wolflike) foxes mostly classified in the genus Dusicyon. The exact position of some species within this scheme is still in doubt, and currently most authorities classify the Arctic, fennec, and bat-eared foxes in genera of their own.

ORDER

Carnivora
(mammalian carnivores)

FAMILY

Canidae
(dogs and their allies)

GENUS

Vulpes

SPECIES

eleven

STEALTHY ELEGANCE

SMALL, AGILE, AND ADAPTABLE, VULPINE FOXES, SUCH AS THE RED FOX (*ABOVE*), ARE IDEALLY QUALIFIED FOR SUCCESS IN A RAPIDLY CHANGING WORLD THAT HAS LITTLE ROOM FOR BIGGER, MORE SPECIALIZED CARNIVORES

Whiskers tingling, a slender vixen stalks a mouse through rough grass, creeping silently with the poise and tail-twitching tension of a cat. Her ears tracking every rustle, she tenses and leaps, propelling herself into the air with her long hind legs and punching down to pin the mouse to the ground with her forefeet. A couple of snaps and it is over; the cat becomes a dog again and trots away up the field to slip through a well-used gap in the fence.

The feline stealth of the otherwise doglike foxes has inspired the idea that they are a hybrid form, but this is simply not true: The ancestral lineages of canids and felids diverged over 54 million years ago. Foxes and small cats simply share a taste for small rodents, and, since they are of roughly similar build, they live and hunt in much the same way. But when fox and cat meet—as they do in some suburban areas—the difference between the two types of carnivores is immediately obvious.

705

The Cape fox's large ears help keep it cool in the southern African deserts by radiating heat.

It's that narrow, foxy muzzle. A cat kills with its long, stabbing canine teeth, and its jaw is shortened to exert sufficient biting pressure. In the process it has lost the grinding molars at the back of the jaw, but cats can easily digest meat without chewing it first. By contrast, the foxes have retained their grinding molars and their jaws and muzzles are longer, enabling them to process a wide range of animal and even plant matter. Because the canine teeth are some distance from the jaw hinge, they cannot exert great pressure; instead they are used to grab the prey and hold it until the fox is in a position to deliver a lethal bite with its powerful carnassials.

While the cats have become specialized killers, many with the power to subdue large animals single-handedly, the foxes have developed as opportunists. With their weaker jaws and slight frame they rarely kill prey larger than themselves, and although some other canids have overcome this by hunting in packs, the foxes have not taken this option. Because they are relatively small canids—compared to wolves, for example—they are easily satisfied with small prey animals, which are best stalked alone.

Anthony Bannister/NHPA

Jeff Lepore/Oxford Scientific Films

A gray fox pup pauses at the den entrance, with the alert expression so typical of vulpines (above).

There are about 40 different varieties of red fox, each with its own distinctive coat (below).

Wayne Lankinen/Aquila Photos

In this they resemble *Hesperocyon* (dawn dog), an ancestor of all modern canids, which skulked around in the forests of North America some 35 million years ago. *Hesperocyon* probably used its array of teeth to slice and crunch through a range of foods, including insect grubs, fruit, worms, small mammals, lizards, frogs, and carrion, and was agile enough to climb trees and search for food through the foliage. This way of life has been inherited almost intact by the gray or tree fox of North and Central America. This fox evolved over 6 million years ago, well before all other surviving canids, and uniquely it has retained the ability to rotate its forefeet, enabling it to grip the trunks of slender trees and scramble up into the branches. It exploits this odd talent to the full, moving nimbly aloft in a most uncanine fashion.

Most other modern canids have lost the ability to climb, having traded it for enhanced running performance. Their limbs are long and they run on their toes for speed. To reinforce their forelimbs two wrist bones are fused and the long "forearm" bones are locked to prevent rotation. The foxes have retained partly retractile claws, whereas the dogs have developed sturdy, nonretractile claws for traction.

RISE OF THE VULPINES

Retractile claws is just one of the subtle distinctions between the foxes (or vulpine canids) and the dogs (or lupine canids). The two diverged 5 to 6 million years ago, a period when the canids in general spread from

North America into Eurasia via the Bering Strait land bridge. Both lineages flourished on both sides of the Pacific, giving rise to a range of species including modern wolves, jackals, dogs, and foxes.

The vulpine foxes split into two main lineages 4 to 5 million years ago. One branch gave rise to the Cape fox, which in turn probably gave rise to Blanford's fox, Bengal fox, pale fox, and fennec. The other branch culminated in the red fox, the biggest and most adaptable of the foxes. Ranging over the entire northern hemisphere, it probably gave rise to the swift and kit foxes of North America, as well as the corsac fox of the Russian steppes and the Tibetan sand fox of the Himalayan foothills. The red fox line also produced the miniature sand fox of North Africa and the Middle East, and, at the other climatic extreme, the polar-adapted arctic fox.

Most of the vulpine foxes are slightly built; even the big red fox is a lightweight compared to a lupine canid of similar size. A small coyote, for example, may be the same length as a red fox but weigh twice as much. This slim elegance lies at the root of their success, giving them a winning combination of agility and opportunism. In fact, the red fox is the most successful of all carnivores today. ■

THE FOXES' FAMILY TREE

The canids can be divided into two main branches: the lupine (wolflike) branch and the vulpine (foxlike) branch. The vulpine foxes form the single genus Vulpes; *they have narrow muzzles, large ears, and slender builds. Wolves typify the lupine branch of the canids, a branch that includes all the wild dogs, wolves, and coyotes, many of which live and hunt in packs.*

BENGAL FOX
Vulpes bengalensis
(VUL-pez ben-gahl-EN-sis)

Considered the most typical of the vulpine foxes, this slender fox forages for a wide assortment of foods in a variety of habitats across the Indian subcontinent. Like all foxes it has a long, slender muzzle and acute senses for detecting the small prey that form the bulk of its diet.

BAT-EARED FOX   FENNEC FOX

ARCTIC FOX

AFRICAN WILD DOG

DOMESTIC DOG

DINGO

RED FOX

Vulpes vulpes
(VUL-pez VUL-pez)

The largest and most widespread of the foxes, the red fox has proved to be the most adaptable and successful carnivore in the modern world. Despite persecution it thrives in landscapes that have been intensively farmed for centuries, and in some countries it has even colonized city centers and industrial parks.

OTHER SPECIES:
CAPE FOX
GRAY FOX
SAND FOX

SOUTH AMERICAN
FOX

COYOTE

WOLF

JACKAL

ALL DOGS (CANIDS)

ⒶNCESTORS

THE DAWN DOG

Leaping through the trees like a cat, the American gray fox is the nearest modern equivalent of *Hesperocyon*, the dawn dog, which appeared in North America some 35 million years ago. The ancestor of all modern canids, *Hesperocyon* was a slender, low-slung creature that hunted through the dense forests that cloaked the northern hemisphere at the time, and probably climbed trees to reach ripe fruit and birds' eggs. With its long muzzle and full battery of teeth, it was well equipped to deal with a wide range of foods. Modern foxes live in much the same way: as opportunist, small-scale foragers. This is one reason why the vulpine foxes are considered slightly more "primitive" than pack-hunting dogs.

ANATOMY:
THE RED FOX

The largest of the vulpine foxes is the red fox (above left), which typically grows to a head-and-body length of 26 in (66 cm) and a weight of 13 lb (6 kg). Occasionally the red fox may grow to twice this weight. The smallest fox in the genus Vulpes is the fennec fox (above right), which grows to a head-and-body length of up to 15.5 in (39 cm) and may weigh as little as 1.8 lb (0.8 kg).

FOREFOOT   **HIND FOOT**

FEET AND TRACKS
The fox's tracks can easily be confused with those of a small dog. However, the fox leaves a more oval, less broad print, with the central two toes placed some way ahead of the other two. When walking or trotting, its tracks form a straight line. The hind prints are placed upon the foreprints, and, as a result, each footprint may misleadingly show five toes.

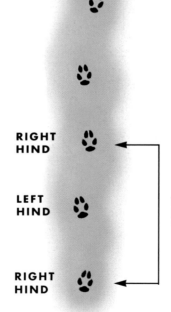

RIGHT HIND

LEFT HIND

RIGHT HIND

WALKING STRIDE: 10-14 IN

THE EARS
are large, mobile, and forward-facing for picking up and locating the sound of moving prey. A fox's ears can even detect the whisper of an earthworm stretching in the grass.

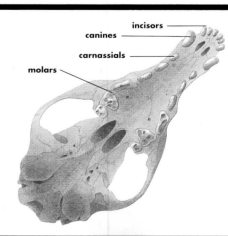

THE MUZZLE
is long and slender, adapted for probing crevices and gripping prey rather than strength and killing power.

RED FOX SKELETON
The leaping method employed by foxes to hunt small prey has favored a lightweight build, and a fox's slender leg bones are far lighter than those of other canids. The vertebrae in the shoulder region have long dorsal processes that act as anchors for strong muscles, enabling the fox to carry heavy prey in its teeth as it trots back to the den.

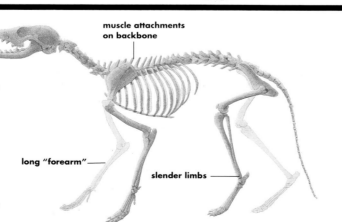

muscle attachments on backbone

long "forearm"

slender limbs

incisors

canines

carnassials

molars

THE EYES

are amber with vertically slit pupils. A reflective tapetum behind the retina increases their sensitivity in the dark. They face forward to provide the binocular, distance-judging vision essential for a hunter.

THE BODY

is lightly built compared to most canids, saving weight and giving the fox great agility on its feet. The light build also reduces the fox's energy needs, enabling it to thrive on small game and scraps.

THE HIND LEGS

are proportionately longer than those of most canids to provide the springing power for the fox's characteristic "mouse leap" hunting technique.

THE FEET

are small and delicate, with semiretractile claws. Dark fur clothing the feet and lower legs can create the impression that the fox is wearing boots.

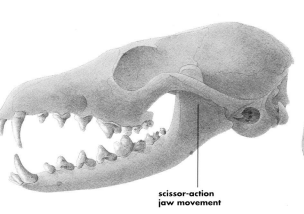

FACT FILE:

THE RED FOX

CLASSIFICATION

GENUS: *VULPES*
SPECIES: *VULPES*

SIZE

HEAD–BODY LENGTH: 22–30 IN (56–76 CM)
TAIL LENGTH: 11–19 IN (28–48 CM)
AVERAGE WEIGHT/MALE: 14 LB (6.4 KG)
AVERAGE WEIGHT/FEMALE: 12 LB (5.5 KG)

COLORATION

VARIABLE, BUT TYPICALLY PALE YELLOW RED TO DEEP RED BROWN ON THE UPPER PARTS AND WHITE OR GRAY WHITE BENEATH. THE FEET AND LOWER LEGS ARE USUALLY BLACK, THE EAR TIPS ARE OFTEN BLACK, AND THE TAIL TIP IS USUALLY WHITE. ALL-BLACK FOXES OCCUR, WHILE THE SILVER FOX HAS BLACKISH FUR WITH WHITE TIPS

FEATURES

LITHE, SLENDER BUILD
LONG, SLIM LEGS
SLENDER MUZZLE
LARGE EARS

THE TAIL

or "brush" is bushy and luxuriant. It acts as a rudder when the fox leaps to pounce on its victims. A large scent gland on the upper surface is marked by a dark patch.

RED FOX SKULL *(left and right)*

The fox has a long jaw with limited movement from side to side. This scissors action ensures the shearing efficiency of the carnassials, but it means that the fox cannot chew its food. The jaw is closed by heavy muscles attached to the crest at the back of the cranium, enabling the molar teeth at the back of the jaw to exert considerable pressure.

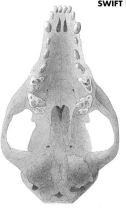

scissor-action jaw movement

SWIFT FOX SKULL

Another vulpine, the swift fox differs from the red fox in the nature of its skull—along with being smaller. A denizen of semiarid and prairie regions, it relies on its full range of teeth to dispatch a wide variety of prey.

FREE ENTERPRISE

THE ABILITY TO EAT VIRTUALLY ANYTHING, ANYWHERE, HAS ENABLED THE FOXES TO FLOURISH IN SOME UNLIKELY HABITATS. INDEED, THE RED FOX IS THE MOST WIDESPREAD CARNIVORE ON EARTH

S tealthily, with measured footfalls, a red fox steals across a darkened, dew-soaked pasture. At intervals it pauses, head cocked, listening. It moves on, stops again, takes another step—then freezes, foot raised, ears twitching, riveted to the patch of grass directly beneath its sharp snout. After a moment of quivering anticipation it plunges down, snatching and pulling. It pauses briefly, then steadily hauls forth its prize: an earthworm.

SLY OPPORTUNIST

A worm may not seem much of a catch for a fully qualified carnivore. Such prey does not fit the image of the ravening fox, terror of hen house and rabbit warren. But foxes have made a profession of behaving in unexpected ways. They are not bound to any particular set of rules, and if a traditional food source fails them they will switch to another, however improbable. Many foxes exploit a succession of temporary resources on a regular basis, developing skills to deal with each. Worm-catching, for example, does not come naturally to a young fox: It is a skill that must be perfected by practice. Such enterprise takes intelligence, and the fox's reputation for sly cunning is well earned. The real talent of the fox, however, is recognizing and taking advantage of opportunities when they arise; the true measure of an opportunist.

The vulpine foxes are among the most adaptable of all mammals. Some have become specialized to particular habitats, but even these specialists have retained a high degree of flexibility to exploit alternative food resources. Other species, such as the red fox, seem to be able to live almost anywhere and eat virtually anything except high-fiber plant matter, which they cannot digest. Red foxes have been found with their stomachs full of blackberries, and Blanford's fox has a notorious taste for grapes, melons, and capers. All foxes devour insects with relish,

and urban foxes may live on a diet of discarded fast food for weeks on end.

The red fox has been recorded at about 74°N on the Tamyr peninsula in northern Siberia, and even on the sea ice of the Arctic Ocean some 60 miles (96 km) north of the Siberian coast, yet the same species also occurs in the valley of the Nile and flourishes in the scorched deserts of the Australian outback. Such a range not only shows remarkable climatic tolerance but also a capacity and willingness to eat a wide variety of foods.

The habits of foxes reflect this basic flexibility, for although each species has typical patterns of behavior, the activities of individuals are prompted by necessity rather than a genetic blueprint. Their ranges, feeding preferences, activity patterns, denning habits, social structures, and breeding strategies are all variable to suit their circumstances.

Ever alert to intruders, a gray fox nurses her cubs (above) *on the arid Colorado plains.*

Andy Rouse/NHPA

Brian Kenney/Planet Earth Pictures

OPEN OPTIONS

Over millenia, many animals adapt physically to exploit particular habitats and food resources. This may give them a big advantage in their own field, but makes them highly vulnerable to environmental change. In the long term, specialization often provides a nonstop ticket to extinction.

By contrast, the foxes have been given the equivalent of a bus pass: They may not live in style, but they can go wherever they like. Their physical adaptations do not equip them to do anything superbly well—except catching voles, perhaps—but their acute intelligence enables them to make the most of unexpected situations. Intelligence is an adaptation like any other, but it has the advantage of being infinitely flexible. In the wild this advantage may be minimal, but in the shifting environments fashioned by humans, a species that can alter its entire behavior pattern at short notice is equipped with a passport to survival.

Red foxes, for example, are traditionally regarded as basically solitary animals, in sharp contrast with the pack-hunting wolves and wild dogs, but recent behavioral studies have shown that foxes often live in small groups. Each group shares a foraging range, and the size of the group is partly determined by the food available within that range. An area with limited food resources will support few foxes—maybe a solitary individual or a pair—but where food is abundant and diverse, some of the young foxes, usually females, may remain within their parents' territory when they mature. This inhibits their breeding behavior, but they may compensate for this by helping to rear their mother's cubs who, after all, are their own kin.

Such an extended family group is a lot like a small wolf pack, and, although foxes do not use the cooperative hunting strategies typical of wolves, they do employ a complex repertoire of sounds, expressions, and body gestures for communication, implying a sophisticated social structure. All this is a long way from the image of the solitary fox, yet that image is not a false one: It simply reflects one of many lifestyles adopted by this enterprising animal. ■

A red fox quenches its thirst. Foxes will readily cross streams and rivers in order to find new living space.

HABITATS

The foxes are among the most adaptable of the carnivores. The Bengal fox, for example, can thrive in the foothills of the Himalayas or in heavily populated farmland. Capitalizing on this ability to survive almost anywhere, the ancestors of many of today's species moved into marginal, relatively inhospitable regions where they had few competitors, and in the course of time their descendants have become steadily better equipped to deal with the conditions they found there.

Among the vulpine foxes several have become desert specialists, including the Cape fox, Blanford's fox, the sand fox, and, in America, the swift and kit foxes. All these species are experts at scratching a living from arid terrain, feeding on desert rodents, ground-nesting birds, carrion, insects, and fruit. These small foxes need proportionally less food than their bigger cousins; this enables them to thrive in habitats where the pickings are too poor to support the red fox. Small size also confers an agility that enables Blanford's fox, for example, to forage over cliffs in regions that are also frequented by red foxes, and this prevents the two from coming into conflict over the same scarce food resources.

Desert foxes are also well adapted to beating the heat. Compared to the red fox they have large ears; these are equipped with a network of fine blood vessels, which act as radiators to lose excess heat. Thus they do not need to pant, which causes the loss of vital moisture. Some species can also allow their bodies to heat up to well above the optimum temperature before they start to pant heavily, and this helps save moisture. Indeed, desert foxes

A sand fox dozes in the sun, just after the morning mist has cleared from the skies over Oman.

Mike Brown/Oxford Scientific Films

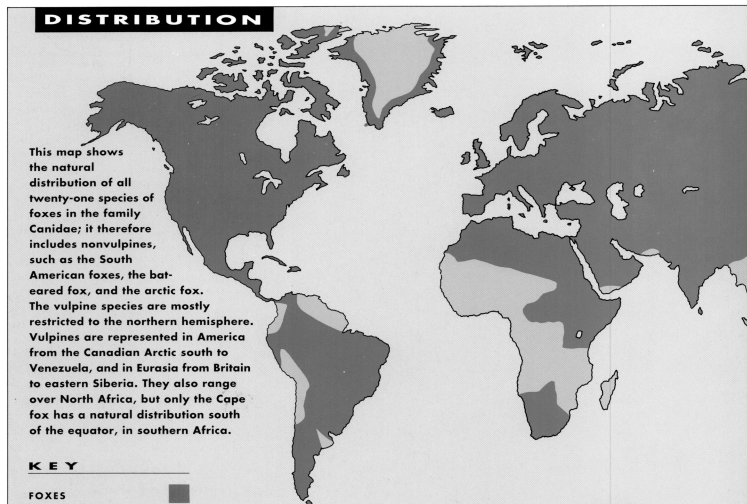

DISTRIBUTION

This map shows the natural distribution of all twenty-one species of foxes in the family Canidae; it therefore includes nonvulpines, such as the South American foxes, the bat-eared fox, and the arctic fox. The vulpine species are mostly restricted to the northern hemisphere. Vulpines are represented in America from the Canadian Arctic south to Venezuela, and in Eurasia from Britain to eastern Siberia. They also range over North Africa, but only the Cape fox has a natural distribution south of the equator, in southern Africa.

KEY

FOXES

KEY FACTS

● The red fox has the largest natural distribution of any living terrestrial mammal apart from humans.

● Different fox species seem to regard each other as competitors for the same resources where they occur in the same habitat, and as a general rule the bigger species will attack and even kill the smaller species. One reason for the decline of the swift fox in the prairie states has been the southward spread of the red fox.

● Urban foxes normally coexist quite peacefully with domestic cats, but if there is a dispute between the two, the cat will often drive the fox away, even though it is smaller.

● In Australia the introduced fox population poses a grave threat to many of the native mammals and birds. Several species of wallabies have now been virtually eradicated from the mainland because of fox predation; they now thrive only on fox-free offshore islands.

rarely—if ever—need to drink: They can satisfy all their moisture needs from the food they eat. It also helps that foxes are by nature nocturnal.

Desert foxes are widely distributed in arid and semiarid regions, rarely straying into steppe grassland and scrub. These are the province of typically larger, less specialized, and therefore more adaptable species such as the corsac and the Bengal foxes. The corsac occurs across the steppes of central Asia, from the Black Sea east to northern Manchuria, favoring open grassland and avoiding farmland. It shares some of the drought-resistant characteristics of the true desert foxes—it can survive long periods without a drink—and thrives in subdesert zones where it appears to roam at will, tending to migrate south in winter when deep snow makes foraging difficult.

The southern margin of the corsac's range is barred by the Tibetan plateau and the Himalayas, province of the Tibetan sand fox. Probably descended from corsac stock, this is a high-altitude specialist rarely found below 10,000 ft (3,000 m) and therefore restricted to the alpine grasslands and rocky slopes of Tibet and Nepal. These regions are also deserts of a kind, but scorching heat is not characteristic, so the Tibetan sand fox does not sport the large ears of the arid-land species. Farther south still, the less demanding and more varied terrain of the Indian subcontinent hosts the Bengal fox. This occupies roughly the same

The Bengal fox makes its home in India, Nepal, and Bangladesh south of the Himalayas.

niche as the corsac fox to the north, but although it favors open grassland and scrub with scattered trees, it is also widespread on agricultural land near human settlements and has become adept at exploiting the habitats created by man.

REDS AROUND THE WORLD

The real opportunist in this respect, however, is the red fox. Normally much bigger than the desert specialists, it is less suited to the marginal conditions of the arid regions and also gives way to the smaller Arctic fox on the exposed tundra and polar deserts of the far north. But within these limits—the boundaries of its climatic range—it is the most successful carnivore on earth, with a natural distribution that is, or was, exceeded only by that of the wolf.

Throughout the northern hemisphere above a latitude of some 30° north, and thriving also in Australia, the red fox has colonized every habitat from lowland swamps to rocky mountainsides and from fertile farmland to the shores of the Dead Sea. In general it prefers to range over a mix of woodland and grassland, but it also flourishes in towns where large yards provide plenty of prey and cover. In several areas such habitats support red foxes living at unusually high densities, although their elusiveness ensures that they are rarely seen.

D. T. Grewcock/Frank Lane Picture Agency

FOCUS ON

THE ENGLISH OAK WOOD

English oaks originally grew in great forests throughout the lowlands. The surviving forests and oak woods are among the richest of English wild habitats. Moth caterpillars swarm over the tender new foliage in spring, while birds search the tree canopy for the insects and breed among the smaller trees and shrubs, such as hazel, that flourish in the dappled understory. Insects, birds, and small mammals, root through the leaf litter for fungi, nuts, larvae, and earthworms. Plants on the forest floor also support these populations.

This rich habitat provides a wealth of food for the red fox, particularly along the borders and in clearings, which attract a wider variety of prey species. The woodland also provides valuable cover, a fact recognized by the hunting landowners of the 19th century who deliberately planted small patches of woodland among their fields to harbor foxes. Today many of these "coverts" have developed into mature oak woods that provide havens for all kinds of wildlife, including foxes, in a hostile world of mechanized agriculture and urban sprawl.

FOREST LEVELS

CANOPY (OAK)

SHRUB LAYER

FOREST FLOOR

An oak forest has three basic layers of vegetation. The layers of oak foliage form the high canopy; beneath this is the shrub layer, typically of hazel, buckthorn, and *climbing honeysuckle with bramble in the clearings. The lowest level, the forest floor, supports a rich flora of herbaceous plants that varies with the soil type.*

Even inner cities have their vulpine representatives. Although many fall victim to traffic accidents, these urban foxes suffer little persecution; enjoy dry, warm accommodation; and have access to rich food resources ranging from vermin and insects to scraps and discarded hamburgers provided by sympathetic householders. Such food is there for the taking, and the fox, opportunist as ever, has moved in to take it. To a fox a town is just another habitat, but with richer pickings than most. ∎

NEIGHBORS

Oak trees support a rich and diverse fauna, from the roots to the crown. In addition, the litter of leaves and fallen, decaying timber are host to additional species that help return nutrients to the soil.

FROG

The frog emerges on warm, damp nights in moist oak woods to hunt for insects, slugs, and worms.

TAWNY OWL

With its keen eyesight and acute hearing, the tawny owl is a superb nocturnal predator of voles and other mice.

Neighbors illustrations Joanne Cowne, Chris Christoforou, Andrew Robinson, and Edwina Goldstone

ENGLISH OAKS
In addition to beech and ash, oaks feature widely in Welsh and English woodlands. They are scarcer in Ireland and Scotland, where coniferous trees dominate. There are two basic types of oaks in Britain: pedunculated and sessile. In the former the acorns hang on stalks, while in the latter they attach directly to the twig.

OAK WOODS

EASTERN GRAY SQUIRREL

The gray squirrel thrives in woodlands where it feeds on acorns, shoots, bark, buds, and flowers.

JAY

The noisy jay buries acorns to provide stores of winter food. Many of these sprout, uneaten, into new oaks.

OAK GALL WASP

The eggs laid by this wasp raise up bulbous growths on oak twigs; the wasp grubs feed inside these.

PURPLE HAIRSTREAK

Although associated with oak trees, this butterfly is rarely seen because it flies so high in the canopy.

WOODPECKER

Woodpeckers thrive in oak woodlands, where they hammer into old timber for grubs under the bark.

HUNTING

A fox may be prepared to eat almost anything, but by instinct it is a hunter. Like a cat, its attention is caught by any flicker of movement, any rustle in the grass, any scent of possible prey. And once alerted, it concentrates on its target, dedicated to follow through to the kill.

Foxes are solitary hunters. They concentrate on small prey that are easy to kill but often difficult to find, so they rely on their acute senses and experience rather than sheer strength, stamina, or tactics. In this they differ from the larger, more social canids like the wild dogs of the African savannas, which prey mainly on large animals that are easy to find

---

ON ONE OCCASION FORTY-EIGHT VOLES WERE RECOVERED FROM THE STOMACH OF A SINGLE RED FOX

---

but difficult to kill. A wild dog needs muscle rather than stealth, and since it is a relatively lightweight animal, it hunts in packs to tackle prey. A fox has enough muscle for its purposes, but it needs to creep unseen upon its victims, and a pack of fellow hunters would be a hindrance rather than a help.

LEAPING

The fox will take almost anything it can catch, but each species has its specialties. The red fox is a professional hunter of voles and will seek them out in preference to other mice and other small prey. It may be that they taste better; foxes are certainly very particular in this respect: They rarely eat shrews and moles because of their unsavory scent glands. They may kill them, but they often discard them when they discover their mistake.

Such mistakes are common because foxes hunt largely by sound, at night. Voles spend most of their lives nibbling shoots and seeds in runs beneath the ground vegetation, and they are generally nearly invisible to a fox. The vole betrays its presence by incautious rustlings and perhaps a faint drift of scent; the fox pricks up its ears and swivels to focus on the sound source: every sense alert, yet absolutely still. Once it has pinpointed the prey, it stalks closer until it is within range, then leaps.

This "mouse leap" is the trademark of the red fox. A startled mouse or vole tends to jump vertically out of danger, a tactic that often enables it to escape a lateral attack. The fox, however, overcomes this by pouncing vertically, so as the terrified

Prey illustrations Ruth Grewcock. Beetles Dan Wright

rodent leaps skyward it collides with the fox coming down. The fox's weight smacks it into the ground and often kills it instantly, saving the fox the trouble of dealing with a struggling victim.

The vertical pounce is a sophisticated maneuver. Instead of merely lunging, the fox launches itself at a carefully judged angle of, on average, about 40 degrees. It may leap up to sixteen feet (5 m), beating its big bushy tail to steer in midair and ensure it lands on target.

DINING DIVERSITY

The leaping tactic probably influenced the fox's evolution, for not only is it lighter than other canids of comparable size, it also has proportionally longer hind legs, which give it extra jumping power. But it is not tied to the technique of stalking and leaping; it uses a whole repertoire of hunting tactics ranging from ambush to dash-and-grab, depending on the prey. Foxes have been known to play dead to lure carrion-eating birds, leaping up and seizing them when they venture within range. A fox will career through a group of feeding rabbits to snatch the least alert, and at the other extreme it may pick its way across a twilit pasture searching for earthworms, nipping them delicately between its front teeth and hauling them intact from the soil.

Earthworms are surprisingly important to some foxes. One study revealed that on old pastureland in central England, near Oxford, red

THE POUNCE

If the fox is pouncing on crusted snow, it may leap at a higher angle, but a forty-degree takeoff (below) usually provides the ideal trajectory for maximum range combined with a vertical landing.

PREY

The red fox's diet is literally limitless in its scope. It includes live invertebrates, mammals, and birds, as well as carrion, fruit, and even food waste from garbage cans. Other vulpines are similarly flexible.

EARTHWORMS

RABBITS

in S I G H T

HIDING THE SPOILS

A fox rarely shares its kill, except with its young, and if it cannot finish a meal in one sitting it will bury or hide the rest for later. A fox raiding a seabird breeding colony will even carry eggs away one by one and bury them individually. A fox rarely, if ever, forgets the location of such a food cache. What is more, these secret caches are rarely found by other foxes except by accident.

Foxes often hide surplus food and return for it later the same night, but a cache may be left for several days or even weeks. In the icy north these stores are a vital insurance against winter food shortages, since the frozen contents stay fresh for months. But foxes are not squeamish about their food: They will devour a rotting carcass with as much relish as a gourmet eating a well-matured cheese.

A red fox crunches on the remains of a moorhen that it caught on the riverbank (above).

foxes were obtaining about half their daily food needs from worms, with a fox eating as many as 146 in a single night. By contrast, foxes on the fells of Cumbria in northern England were living mainly on rabbits and grouse, and analysis of their scats (feces) showed no trace of earthworms.

Other species are equally unpredictable. The scats of Bengal foxes contained the remains of beetles, grasshoppers, crabs, lizards, rats, and mice, as well as odd fragments of ants, termites, spiders, and scorpions. These foxes may also take snakes and birds, as well as fruits such as melons. In Oklahoma, swift foxes prey heavily on birds, and a stomach-content analysis of eighteen corsac foxes in the Transbaikalia region of the former U.S.S.R. revealed the remains of polecats and even other corsac foxes. ■

FIELD VOLE	BIRDS' EGGS	FROGS	PHEASANTS	BEETLES	FIELD MICE

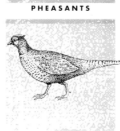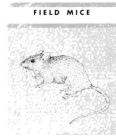

Main illustration Peter David Scott/Wildlife Art Agency

719

SOCIAL STRUCTURE

As lone hunters of small prey, foxes rarely need to roam widely, for voles and rabbits generally stay put. They are patchily distributed, however, and a fox that finds a rich concentration of prey—or any other food—has every reason to defend the area as a feeding territory. Two pairs of eyes offer more effective policing than one, and since two foxes can usually feed within much the same area as an individual, the typical pattern of fox society worldwide is the monogamous pair.

But patterns are made to be broken. While red foxes nearly always forage alone, they often live in groups, sharing a territory and defending it against other groups. Groups vary in size: In areas where food is scarcer and the foxes suffer a high mortality rate, they tend to live in elusive, fast-breeding pairs; but where there is enough food and little need for early breeding, they may associate in groups of up to six adults, plus, typically, a single litter of cubs.

This tendency arises partly from the red fox's flexible feeding habits. A typical fox exploits a variety of food sources, turning to each as it becomes available. Thus, each animal needs a feeding territory that offers an adequate choice. So a territory for a single fox or pair might include, say, a worm-rich pasture (worms emerge on warm, damp nights), a rabbit warren (rabbits rarely feed in the rain), a breeding site for ground-nesting birds (restricted to the breeding season), and a yard where food scraps are provided in winter.

STAY-AT-HOME YOUNGSTERS

Such a territory ensures a steady food supply, but on any night the sheer quantity of food available is more than enough for a pair. This gives young foxes—the pair's cubs from the previous season—a strong motive for staying at home, particularly if the wider area is well populated with foxes and has a low rate of persecution, disease, or road casualties, meaning that vacant territories are scarce. Dispersing in search of territories is a risky business, and if there is no vacant habitat nearby many young foxes will stay at home.

But they may not be offered the option: Some young foxes, usually males, are driven from the family group when they mature. Young females, and even the odd male, are often permitted to stay. It may be that young males have a stronger instinct to strike out alone regardless of the risks, but they are also perceived as rivals by the dominant male.

Philip Perry/Frank Lane Picture Agency

Illustration Simon Turvey/Wildlife Art Agency

A Cape fox grooms her cub on returning to the den in the Kalahari, Botswana.

A young fox that stays on its parents' territory has a strictly subordinate role. This involves deferring at all times to the dominant pair and even other subdominants. The high-ranking animals will not hesitate to bully the underdog, which tries to avert their wrath by displays of cringing submission. The lowest subordinate may also be denied access to the best food resources until the others have fed.

Yet despite this rough treatment, subordinate vixens in a group are usually eager to help raise the dominant pair's cubs, which share some of their genes. Their own breeding behavior is usually suppressed, presumably through the influence of the dominant vixen. The resident male will mate with them if the opportunity arises, even though they may be his own daughters. Normally, however, the male ignores the subordinate vixens.

WORTH WAITING FOR

Eventually all the groveling may pay off, for if the dominant vixen dies one of her juniors may get the chance to take her place, enjoy all the benefits of a rich territory, and breed in her turn. Occasionally the social order is turned upside down: In one group of sisters the hierarchy was shuffled regularly, but this rarely happens where the dominant animals are parents of the others. If all else fails a low-ranking fox may give up the struggle and leave, preferring the dangers of rootless independence to the dubious security of a toehold in society. ■

SOCIAL CONSTRAINTS

Only one of these five vixens breeds with the male (center left). The dominant vixen's presence in some way inhibits normal estrus in the subordinate vixens.

721

TERRITORY

A mature fox normally forages over a fairly well-defined home range and rarely travels beyond its boundaries. The extent of a home range depends on the richness of the habitat and the number of foxes in the vicinity. Clearly, the more food there is per square unit of land, the fewer units are required to support a fox; and on rich, varied farmland, a red fox may spend most of its life within an area of less than 100 acres (40 hectares), an area that it could easily run across in a minute. In the Arctic, however, where food is often extremely scarce and subject to wide seasonal fluctuations, an individual fox may have a home range of up to 8,400 acres (3,400 hectares).

Between these extremes the ranges regularly traversed by red foxes give an intriguing insight into the food resources available. On the windswept uplands of mid-Wales, for example, red fox ranges average some 1,000 acres (400 hectares), but on the agriculturally productive cereal prairies of North Dakota, they average 4,900 acres (2,000 hectares). Perhaps most surprising are the ranges regularly covered by urban foxes: In residential areas of Bristol, England, the local foxes range over 60–96 acres (24–39 hectares), indicating that towns are among the richest of all fox habitats.

One of the largest ranges recorded for a red fox was that of a male in the deserts of Oman, which spanned 12,350 acres (5,000 hectares). Obviously such

A red fox's feces smell highly distinctive—even to human noses—and provide effective scent marks.

D. T. Grewcock/Frank Lane Picture Agency

(in) SIGHT

SOLITARY NOMADS

Some foxes wander over the landscape, feeding and denning where they can. These itinerants are usually young males leaving the areas where they were born, and although many eventually settle down, they may travel a long way before finding vacant territories.

The record for a red fox is a straight-line distance of 310 miles (500 km), recorded in Sweden; and since many foxes zigzag as they disperse, this particular individual may have traveled much farther. On average, dispersing males cross the width of four to six territories.

BOXING FOXES

Intrusive neighbors will often incur a red fox's wrath, especially those that are caught trespassing on prime sectors of its territory. Fortunately, these skirmishes usually involve more barking than biting (left).

SCENT MESSAGES

By marking its territory, a fox helps keep neighboring foxes informed and, ideally, out of sight (below).

a vast area cannot be adequately defended: The borders are too long, and many parts of the range may be visited only rarely. In such cases some overlap between neighboring ranges is inevitable and will be tolerated by a resident fox as long as any intruders avoid the core areas—the favored parts of the range where the resident spends most of its time. Some species or populations are highly tolerant in this respect. Kit foxes in California were seen to be using home ranges with a wide overlap, and foxes from different groups hunted in the same areas—although not simultaneously. Others are less casual. In the study of a group of sand foxes in Oman, neighboring pairs patrolled their range boundaries, barking defiance at each other.

A FLEXIBLE RESPONSE

Many foxes aim to defend their entire feeding range as exclusive territory. This may be prompted by the close proximity of neighboring foxes; but the more potential trespassers there are, the harder the job of territorial defense. This might encourage the residents to make the territory as small as possible, shortening the borders for improved security.

Among group-living red foxes studied on farmland in central England, the territorial boundaries were often precisely delineated, with the border between two adjacent group territories running down a fence line, a ditch, or a bank. These populations were relatively stable, so the rival claims over marginal areas had probably been resolved over time. In less stable populations the situation tends to be more fluid as residents die and neighbors move in: Among urban foxes, for example, where road casualties are common, individual ranges tend to drift as the foxes move to vacated areas. These foxes also tend to be less territorial, although, like the kit foxes in California, they are careful to avoid each other in areas where ranges overlap.

If neighbors do encounter one another, there may be a fight. Neighbors of the same sex are often particularly hostile, charging into an attack, sparring on their hind legs like boxers, and snapping at each other's muzzles. They rarely do any serious damage, however, and normally one of the combatants backs down and, to the accompaniment of screams and snarls, retreats across the territorial boundary with the victor on his or her heels.

SINCE RED FOXES OFTEN LIVE IN GROUPS WHERE POPULATIONS ARE ESPECIALLY DENSE, THEY CAN RELY ON THE EXTRA FOXPOWER TO DEFEND THE HOME RANGE

Even though such conflicts rarely lead to injuries, they are a waste of time and energy, so foxes minimize them by letting each other know where they are. They do this by scent-marking, using their pungent urine, their feces, the acrid-smelling contents of their anal scent glands, and the relatively fragrant, oily secretions from glands between their toes. The foot glands leave a trail wherever the fox goes (the trail foxhounds follow), but the fox can deposit the other scent marks wherever it sees fit. In practice foxes scent-mark liberally along their trails, on conspicuous objects such as molehills and tufts of grass, and most assiduously along territorial boundaries. Other foxes can recognize the sex and identity of an individual from the marks it leaves, and therefore whether it may be friendly or hostile. The system works so well that members of neighboring groups encounter one another as rarely as once or twice a week, even though their territories may overlap. ∎

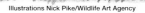

Illustrations Nick Pike/Wildlife Art Agency

REPRODUCTION

Once she is sexually mature, a red fox vixen is receptive once a year, for as little as two or three days. Hormonal rise begins several days before she is ready to mate and her scent marks declare the fact to the local males. Accordingly if any male feels he has a claim on a female—usually the dominant vixen sharing his territory—he has to beware of rivals who might sneak in under his nose.

MATE GUARDING

As the winter breeding season approaches, therefore, a male pays close attention to his intended. They still tend to forage alone, but they may rest or travel together for several hours each night. This "mate guarding" is crucial to the dog fox, for he will shortly invest a lot of time and energy in bringing food to the vixen and her cubs, and he clearly does not want to support the cubs of another male. The female may at first reject the male's advances, spitting and snarling at him despite all his attentions, but persistence usually pays off.

Having mated, the male is likely to slip off in search of other receptive vixens during the 53-day gestation period. But since he can rarely care for more than one brood at once, he may have to use the

AT THE DEN

The dog fox is kept busy bringing food to the vixen and her hungry litter (right).

Wayne Lankinen/Aquila

very trick he was trying to prevent by mate guarding and foist his own offspring onto an unsuspecting male. Not surprisingly, relations between neighboring males reach a low ebb at this time and fights are frequent.

In the United States red fox cubs are born from late February to June, usually in a nursery burrow or earth but occasionally in a tussock of grass or a hollow tree. There may be up to twelve of them, but four to eight is usual. These blind bundles of chocolate fur depend fully on the mother for about four weeks; during this time the male brings food to her. At about one month old the cubs leave their nursery at night to explore; at this time, too, they eat their first solid food and their coats start to redden. By about two months old they have their adult color.

At eight to ten weeks they are weaned, but the parents have to bring their food to the den. Among group-living foxes it is normal for all the adults to bring food to the cubs. At about twelve weeks old the cubs begin to forage with the adults, and the nursery is abandoned. This is a period of intense learning for the cubs. They learn about food; how to avoid their

Helpless at birth, red fox cubs can soon fend for themselves, even at the expense of their siblings.

CUB CALENDAR

DECEMBER
MATING SEASON STARTS; FOXES BECOME MORE TERRITORIAL

JANUARY
THE MAIN MATING PERIOD IN NORTHERN EUROPE

FEBRUARY
PREGNANT VIXENS LOOK FOR SUITABLE NURSERY DENS

MARCH
CUBS ARE BORN TOWARD THE END OF THE MONTH; MALE BRINGS FOOD FOR NURSING VIXEN

APRIL
CUBS MAKE FIRST FORAYS ABOVE GROUND; VIXEN MAY MOVE THEM ELSEWHERE IF SHE FEELS INSECURE OR THE DEN IS TOO SMALL

MAY
CUBS START EATING SOLID FOOD AND FIGHT AMONG THEMSELVES FOR DOMINANCE

JUNE
FULLY WEANED CUBS LEAVE THE DEN AND FOLLOW ADULTS AS THEY FORAGE

JULY
CUBS BEGIN FORAGING FOR THEMSELVES

AUGUST
CUBS BECOME INCREASINGLY INDEPENDENT, ALTHOUGH THEY ARE STILL SEQUESTERED WITH A PARENT DURING THE DAY

SEPTEMBER
CUBS FULLY GROWN; DOMINANT CUBS EXERT PRESSURE ON MALE UNDERDOGS TO LEAVE

OCTOBER
START OF DISPERSAL PERIOD. YOUNG FEMALES MAY REMAIN WITH THE FAMILY GROUP

NOVEMBER
DISPERSAL CONTINUES THROUGH TO THE END OF THE YEAR AND THE START OF THE NEXT MATING SEASON

enemies, and how to use the terrain to their advantage. They already know who is boss, for red fox cubs establish a pecking order by fighting in the nursery. These fights are in deadly earnest and can even prove fatal. As they mature they employ more subtle tactics, grooming each other selectively to exclude the underdogs, which may eventually be the first to leave the family group. These refugees are also smaller than the young foxes that remain, suggesting that they have been denied their full share of the food brought back by the adults.

By the end of summer the cubs are fully grown and may eventually seek out territories of their own. This is a dangerous time for a fox: As it moves through unknown terrain it is likely to run into trouble as it trespasses on the territories of other foxes or attracts larger predators and humans. Among urban foxes some 55 percent die in their first year before they get the chance to breed, but some lucky survivors may breed for eight seasons in a row before dying of old age. ■

Illustration Guy Croucher/Wildlife Art Agency

QUIETLY CONFIDENT

THE RED FOX EXHIBITS A RARE TALENT FOR SURVIVAL AGAINST APPARENTLY INSURMOUNTABLE ODDS, AND ITS MORE TIMID RELATIVES WOULD DO WELL TO FOLLOW ITS EXAMPLE

In the suburbs of English cities there are people who put out food for foxes. A fox could live off it for weeks, raise a family, flourish. Those who put out the food congratulate themselves that they have foxes in their backyard, and thrill to the occasional glimpse of a nocturnal visitor stealing across the lawn.

If foxes were given to reflection they would find this deeply baffling. For centuries they have been vilified and persecuted as vermin, and, since the disappearance of the wolf from much of Europe, the red fox has been cast in the role of chief villain among a depleted crew of predators. In sheep country it is hated as a killer of lambs, and among poultry farmers it has a reputation for mass slaughter. People, who harvest game birds for their own survival, resent a creature that regularly preys on young pheasants, partridges, and grouse and take every opportunity to turn their guns on the fox instead.

Meanwhile loss can be turned to profit by selling fox pelts, which fetch a good price. A thriving trade in fox furs during the 1970s encouraged trapping on a massive scale, with 388,643 red foxes and 264,957 gray foxes taken in North America alone during the peak season of 1977–78. Throughout its range the red fox is lucky to survive more than a year without a terminal encounter with a shotgun or snare, and in recent decades the fox's role as an unwitting carrier of rabies has allowed the gunmen to promote vulpicide as a social duty. The resulting carnage has been terrible. Notoriously over 50,000 foxes were killed in Alberta, Canada, in 1952 as part of a rabies control campaign; and throughout Europe foxes are trapped, shot, or gassed like rats in their dens.

In Britain and in North America they are also hunted from the saddle with packs of hounds. Such sport is widely condemned as barbaric, but to its enthusiasts the bloodletting involved is almost incidental to the thrill of the chase and the opportunities it provides for skillful riding. So paradoxically the hunters actually value foxes and may even encourage them in areas where they are scarce. But the general consensus, in rural areas at least, is that the only good fox is a dead one—and the more that are killed the better. This type of attitude has led to the elimination of the wolf from most of its vast natural range and has faced other wild canids such as the African wild dog and the Simien jackal with the prospect of imminent extinction. Yet despite persecution the red fox flourishes. Why?

Basically, the quicker they are killed, the quicker they breed. This is partly because fox territories become vacant on a regular basis, enabling young

A. Toneland/Frank Lane Picture Agency

The highly controversial pursuit of hunting (above) *accounts for about 12,500 fox deaths every year.*

Kenneth W. Fink/Ardea

This map shows how the red fox has colonized all off mainland Australia since its introduction there in the 19th century. Tasmania, however, remains fox free.

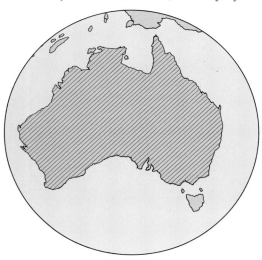

 RED FOX DISTRIBUTION

Pining for the hunting traditions of their homeland, English settlers imported the red fox into Australia in 1868. The fox obligingly invaded every corner of the mainland, and in the process endangered several species of native mammals and birds.

animals to disperse from the parent territory and breed on their own; in areas where foxes live longer the scarcity of vacant territories encourages young foxes to stay at home where their breeding instincts are suppressed. Eliminating foxes also releases prey for the survivors, and this apparently increases the potential number of cubs a vixen can bear and rear. In Germany, for example, the average litter size among foxes living at high density in forested areas is three to four cubs; but in open-field areas where they are subject to heavy hunting, the average number of cubs in a litter is six.

This capacity to offset casualties is common among wild animals, but the red fox seems particularly well equipped to exploit it. Its small size may be a factor: Since it is relatively inconspicuous and able to thrive on small prey and scraps, it can live in large populations that provide a continuous source of healthy new breeding stock. Among wolves, by contrast, minimum viable populations of 500 or so

The corsac fox may well be threatened as a species. Hunted widely for its luxuriant pelt, it is also a victim of traps set for other fur-bearing mammals.

John Downer/Oxford Scientific Films

animals are restricted to wilderness regions, and smaller populations surviving in less remote areas are likely to suffer the corrosive effects of inbreeding. The red fox's elusiveness and opportunism have also allowed it to live on man's doorstep among

ALONGSIDE MAN

RABIES

Over much of its range the red fox is the principal wild carrier of rabies, a disease that kills about 15,000 humans each year. The fox itself dies within a month of infection, but during that time it may infect many other animals.

The current European rabies epidemic erupted in Poland in 1939, reaching France in 1968 and Italy in 1977. Britain has so far escaped, thanks to its island status and strict import laws. In North America rabies is rife among foxes, bats, wolves, coyotes, raccoons, and skunks.

Since rabies in Europe is largely confined to foxes, the authorities have encouraged hunters to shoot foxes on sight. This policy has failed, however, because foxes are such adept survivors. Early attempts to immunize them were hampered by lack of a suitable vaccine. But following recent advances, total immunization of foxes in Europe is now in sight. If this happens, then foxes may soon be spared a good deal of prejudice and persecution.

According to the writer Goethe, the red fox "practices every sort of treachery." Antihero of fables and folk tales through the ages, this lean survivor has won grudging praise from many of its staunchest human enemies.

suburban housing and even in cities. Despite high road casualties these urban foxes flourish, and refugees from city life may help maintain rural populations in areas of intense persecution by farmers.

POOR RELATIONS

Whatever the red fox's secret of success, it is not fully shared by other species. The corsac fox, for example, is similar in many ways: A relatively social animal of open country, it is capable of thriving on a wide range of foods. Yet the corsac seems to be less adaptable. It rarely lives near human habitation, avoids farmland, and has retreated in the face of agricultural exploitation of its steppe habitat. Its decline has been hastened by intensive hunting for its fur and an unfortunate tendency to get caught in traps set for marmots, whose burrows it often adopts as its own. In consequence the corsac fox is considered to be threatened by the International Union for the Conservation of Nature (IUCN), although its precise status is unknown owing to a lack of reliable information.

The pale fox, sand fox, and Blanford's fox appear to be threatened in similar ways, although they share the same vague conservation status as the corsac. Even the Bengal fox, which displays many of the opportunist traits of the red fox, has declined in recent years and found its way into the burgeoning list of species under threat. It seems that however resourceful a wild animal may be, it is doomed to decline in the face of human colonization unless it can find ways of exploiting the changing environment on its own terms—a talent that the red fox consistently displays in abundance. ∎

FOXES IN DANGER

IN 1994, THE INTERNATIONAL UNION FOR THE CONSERVATION OF NATURE (IUCN) CLASSIFIED THE CONSERVATION STATUS OF THE VULPINE FOXES THAT ARE KNOWN OR SUSPECTED TO BE UNDER THREAT:

ISLAND GRAY FOX	RARE
BENGAL FOX	INDETERMINATE
BLANFORD'S FOX	INSUFFICIENTLY KNOWN
CORSAC FOX	INSUFFICIENTLY KNOWN
PALE FOX	INSUFFICIENTLY KNOWN
SAND FOX	INSUFFICIENTLY KNOWN
FENNEC FOX	INSUFFICIENTLY KNOWN

INTO THE FUTURE

The future of the red fox seems to be secure, for despite persecution for its fur, for sport, and as a threat to domestic livestock, it shows no sign of declining. It flourishes in such a huge variety of habitats and over such a vast range that even local extinction through disease or disaster would barely dent the world population, and its ability to thrive in unpromising terrain has ensured a regular exchange of breeding stock between local populations. One of the biggest threats facing wild animals—particularly large carnivores that live at low densities—is the isolation of small populations through habitat erosion and their consequent decline through inbreeding. The red fox is unlikely to suffer from this particular problem, since it will live almost anywhere provided there is sufficient food available to support it and will readily cross unpromising terrain and even colonize it.

PREDICTION

GIVE THEM A CHANCE

The recent return to form of the swift fox in North America is a heartening example of how resilient the vulpines can be. Other foxes currently under threat throughout the world may yet do the same, if we give them the chance.

This willingness to experiment with virtually any food source in any environment is the fox's secret of success. Many wild animals are unwilling or unable to exploit new foods presented in unfamiliar ways, but the red fox has no such inhibitions. While other animals retreat before the changes brought about by man, the red fox simply adapts to exploit them. It has become one of the few species that flourish alongside humans rather than in spite of them, so the continuing expansion of human populations may well help its prospects.

The other vulpines seem less adaptable, but they have been so little studied that we may be ignorant of their true potential. Several species are suspected to be under threat, but information is so scanty that their true status cannot be determined. Many are denizens of arid regions, where they suffer relatively little human interference, and this may be to their advantage. The more remote areas act as refuges and may harbor flourishing populations that have never been reported. ∎

RABIES IN RETREAT

For half a century European foxes have been plagued by rabies, but a solution—immunization—is now a practical proposition. Until recently a large-scale immunization campaign was impossible because there was no effective "killed" vaccine that could be administered orally in bait; the highly effective live vaccine is too dangerous to leave littered around the landscape.

This difficulty, however, has now been overcome. Using a fairly innocuous *Vaccinia* virus that has been genetically engineered to simulate the rabies virus, scientists have found a way of producing an immunity to the disease without exposing animals to the actual organism that causes it. The vaccine is injected into a suitable bait, which is then distributed from aircraft. Early tests indicate that some 80 percent of a local fox population may take the bait and immunize themselves. Judging by the results being achieved in the field, this is quite adequate to stop the disease in its tracks, and it is not impossible that rabies may be eradicated in Europe within the next decade.

LAMB SCAM

Farmers and shepherds have traditionally hated the red fox as a lamb killer. Recent studies in Scotland, however, suggest that shooting foxes to prevent them from killing lambs is pointless. For three years foxes were allowed to breed freely on a large sheep-farming estate while their numbers, feeding habits, and impact on the lambs were closely monitored. The fox population did not increase at all, despite the fact that none were shot; meanwhile, foxes killed fewer lambs than on neighboring estates. Furthermore, previous studies showed that while up to 24 percent of lambs born in the Scottish Highlands may be born dead or die of hypothermia, disease, or malnutrition, less than 2 percent are taken by foxes.

Illustration Kim Thompson

GALAGOS

RELATIONS

Lorisids and tarsiers belong to the prosimian suborder, Prosimii, within the primate order. Other primates include:

LEMURS

INDRIS & SIFAKAS

CAPUCHINS

MARMOSETS

BABOONS

GREAT APES

HUMAN

Tony Stone Worldwide

NIGHT WATCHERS

WHEN NIGHT FALLS, CREATURES WITH STARING EYES LEAP AMONG THE TREES OF AFRICA AND ASIA. NEARLY MONKEYS BUT NOT QUITE, THEY ARE THE LITTLE-KNOWN GALAGOS, OR BUSH BABIES, POTTOS, LORISES, AND TARSIERS

The galagos, pottos, lorises, and tarsiers are among the most curious, yet least studied of the mammals. These shy creatures of the night may at first seem strange, but a close look at their antics, or at their dexterous hands, reveals something hauntingly familiar about them. These animals, like us, are primates, and their appearance and behavior give us some insights into what the forerunners of today's monkeys and apes may have been like.

All galagos, pottos, lorises, and tarsiers are nocturnal forest and woodland dwellers, adapted for climbing and for detecting food in the darkness. They share their habitats with monkeys, their evolutionarily more advanced cousins, but their nighttime habits mean that they seldom come into contact or competition with them. Certain similarities in anatomy and behavior are shared between the galagos, pottos, lorises, and tarsiers, but as we shall see there are also striking differences.

CLASSIFICATION

The galagos, or bush babies, pottos, and lorises on the one hand and the tarsiers on the other are two distinct families of primates (the order that includes monkeys, apes, and humans). Between them, the two families comprise six genera with a total of at least twenty species.

ORDER

Primates
(primates)

SUBORDER

Prosimii

FAMILY

Lorisidae

GENERA

Galago
(galagos)
Perodicticus
(potto)
Arctocebus
(angwantibo)
Loris
(slender loris)
Nycticebus
(slow loris)

FAMILY

Tarsiidae
(tarsiers)

GENUS

Tarsius

The bush babies or galagos of tropical Africa are probably the best-known group. Rather cute in appearance, with large eyes and ears and thick gray, brown, or reddish fur, they range in size from that of a large mouse to that of a cat. Agile and lively, they take refuge in trees and shrubs by day, and come out at night to search the branches for both plant and animal foods. Propelled by long, muscular hind limbs, galagos can run along branches, make impressive leaps between trees, and hop across the ground like tiny kangaroos. Finely tuned senses—excellent eyesight, acute hearing, and a sensitive nose—enable them to dart about and locate food. Their hands and feet are adapted for grasping objects and gripping branches, and flattened pads on the ends of the digits provide the animals with a delicate sense of touch. One toe only on each foot bears a short "toilet claw" that is used for grooming fur around the head. The animal keeps the rest of its coat clean using a special comblike arrangement of its front teeth.

STATUE-STILL

Pottos and lorises, which occur, respectively, in Africa and Asia, are broadly similar to one another. They share the galagos' traits of large, forward-facing eyes, dense fur, touch-sensitive hands and feet, toilet claws, and tooth-combs. But in their manner of getting about they are quite different. They spend long periods motionless or moving very

Stephen Dalton/NHPA

Gary Bell/Planet Earth Pictures

The spectral tarsier (above) *is the world's smallest carnivorous primate.*

732

 **SIGHT**

LEMURS APART

The lemurs are the closest relatives to the galagos, lorises, and pottos. The two sets of animals are similar in many ways and are generally grouped in a single suborder of primates—but they have their differences. While the lemurs and their close allies are confined to the island of Madagascar, the lorisids range across mainland Africa and Asia. Madagascar has been isolated for the last 50 million years, and lemurs have evolved there without competition from more advanced primates. The lorisids that live today on the mainland avoid competition with monkeys through being nocturnal. Lorisids have shorter snouts, more rounded heads, and more forward-facing eyes than the lemurs.

slowly and smoothly along branches. With strong limbs, and hands and feet that give a powerful grip, they can hold seemingly gravity-defying postures for hours on end. The potto and the slow loris have a cat-sized, heavier build with stout limbs, while the angwantibo, or golden potto, and the slender loris are smaller with relatively daintier limbs. All pottos and lorises have short tails. They, together with the galagos, are often known collectively as the lorisids.

LONG TAILS AND DRY SNOUTS
The tarsiers are fundamentally different from the lorisids. Though tarsiers in some ways resemble the smaller galagos, they have long tails, more elongated feet, and especially long, skinny digits. They also have a dry as opposed to moist snout, they lack a tooth-comb, they have two sets of toilet claws on the hind feet and they can move each digit independently of the others. Their eyes are truly enormous, enabling the animals to leap large distances with precision and helping them hunt for nocturnal insects in the rain forests of Indonesia and the Philippines. With their digits spread, tarsiers commonly cling to smooth, vertical tree trunks.

ANCIENT SPECIES
Lorisids, or at least something like them, have been around for a very long time. Galagos are probably the closest representatives we have to the earliest

A lesser galago performs a characteristic body-twist as it leaps from branch to branch.

primates. Fossil forms dating back 60 million years have been found to have dentition very similar to that of the present-day dwarf galagos. Some time later, probably in the Miocene epoch (25–5 million years ago), the slow-moving type of lorisid represented by today's lorises and pottos seems to have evolved. As far as we know, these animals have never spread to the Americas.

Fossil tarsiers, however, have been found in the New World, though the animals do not live there today. Most zoologists now believe tarsiers have long evolved independently from the lorisids. They argue that there is a fundamental division among the primates between the moist-nosed lemurs and lorisids and the dry-nosed tarsiers, monkeys, and apes. The dry-nosed branch first split from the ancestral primate stock, and then itself subdivided

GREATER GALAGO
Galago crassicaudatus
(GAH-lah-go crassy-cow-DAH-tuss)

There are at least eleven, and perhaps as many as sixteen or more, species of galago. Like lorises and pottos they have large eyes, but otherwise differ greatly from them. They have long, tufted tails, long hind legs, and large ears. They move rapidly through the trees by running, climbing, and leaping.

OTHER SPECIES INCLUDE:
LESSER GALAGO
DWARF GALAGO
ALLEN'S GALAGO
NEEDLE-CLAWED
GALAGO

Color illustrations Kim Thompson

SPECTRAL TARSIER
Tarsius spectrum
(TAR-see-uss SPECK-trum)

OTHER SPECIES:
PHILIPPINE TARSIER
WESTERN TARSIER
LESSER SPECTRAL
TARSIER

Four species of tarsier have been discovered across the islands of southeast Asia. Superficially similar to galagos, they have even larger eyes, very long hind limbs, and long, thin tails. They are supreme nocturnal predators, taking a wide range of both vertebrate and invertebrate prey. They are territorial and highly vocal.

FAMILY
TARSIIDAE

MADAGASCAN
PRIMATES

through time—the tarsiers were one of its earliest offshoots. Tarsiers may have existed in Indonesia for 40 million years; they may have originally been active by day, only later turning to night life with the visual adaptations that requires. The species today that seems most primitive, the spectral tarsier, is the least specialized for nocturnal activity.

It is likely that the number of lorisid species recognized by zoologists will remain a rising figure in years to come. Given their nocturnal habits, for example, it is perhaps not surprising that species may be separated from one another not by their visual appearance but by their calls. Not long ago Africa was assumed to have 6 galago species. In 1979, 11 species were distinguished, and research now suggests there could be at least 16. ∎

LEMURS, INDRIS,
SIFAKAS, AYE-AYES

PRIMATES

734

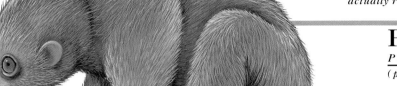

THE LORISID AND TARSIER FAMILY TREE

Along with the lemurs and their relatives, the galagos, pottos, lorises, and tarsiers have often been grouped together as the "prosimians." Though they are primates, they clearly differ from monkeys and apes. But the tarsiers also differ in crucial ways from the galagos and lorises. Confusion also arises at the species and genus levels, particularly among the galagos. Recent analysis of calls suggests that animals seemingly identical in appearance may actually represent a number of different species.

POTTO
Perodicticus potto
(peh-ro-DICK-tick-uss POT-o)

The potto and the angwantibo or golden potto, Arctocebus calabarensis, occur in Africa. The potto is larger and has more robust limbs than the angwantibo, the two **differing from one another in much the same way as their Asian equivalents, the lorises. Pottos move slowly and have short tails, large eyes, and pincer-gripping hands.**

SLOW LORIS
Nycticebus coucang
(nick-tih-SEE-buss KOO-kang)

There are three species of loris, found in the tropical forests of Asia. They are usually grouped with the pottos in the subfamily Lorisinae. Lorises are slow-moving climbing animals, with very short tails, pincerlike grips of their hands and feet, and large, forward-pointing eyes specially adapted for nighttime vision.

OTHER SPECIES:
SLENDER LORIS
PYGMY SLOW LORIS

FAMILY
LORISIDAE

HIGHER
PRIMATES
(ANTHROPOIDEA)

NEW WORLD MONKEYS

OLD WORLD MONKEYS

APES

ANATOMY: THE LESSER GALAGO

The slow loris (below left) reaches 12 in (30 cm) from head to rump, with a 2 in (5 cm) tail. The Phillipine tarsier (below right) has a head-and-body length of 5 in (13 cm), with a tail up to 10 in (25 cm) long. The dwarf galago (below center) has similar proportions, but is a little smaller all around.

THE NOSE

is moist—tarsiers have a dry nose—and provides a keen sense of smell.

THE EARS

are large and batlike. The galago can retract these out of harm's way when subduing large, flapping insects. Folds within the ear improve sound orientation, making the ears exceptionally sensitive organs for tracking insects moving in the dark.

THE EYES

are huge, letting in plenty of light when necessary. They face forward, giving an excellent sense of distance. This helps galagos and tarsiers to judge leaps and bounds accurately, even in near-complete darkness.

GALAGO

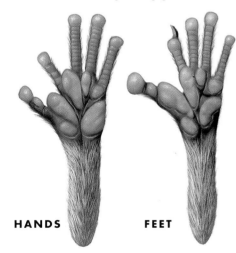

HANDS   FEET

Galagos, pottos, and lorises have large, opposable thumbs enabling them to grasp objects. Each digit of the hand and foot has a nail, except for the second toe which has a "toilet" claw used for grooming the head, neck, and ears—where the tooth-comb cannot reach. Flattened pads on the ends of the digits provide the animals with a delicate sense of touch.

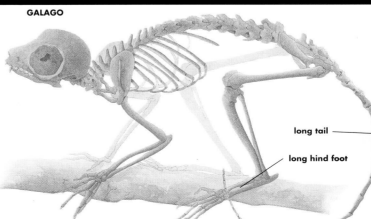

X-RAY

SKELETON
The galago's skeleton clearly shows the longer length of the hind limbs, especially of the foot segment, giving the animal strong propulsion when leaping. The long tail is also important during leaps when it acts as a balancing device.

GALAGO

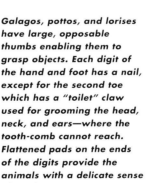

long tail

long hind foot

SKULLS
The skull of the galago has a fairly short snout and rounded braincase. The large eye sockets are ringed with a prominent ridge. The tarsier also has a short snout, and its eye sockets are extremely large, with pronounced rims and only a narrow ridge separating the two. Each enormous eye is similar in weight to the animal's brain.

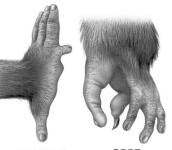

HANDS **FEET**
·POTTO

The hands and feet of pottos and lorises can exert a firm grip on tree trunks, enabling them to creep slowly about the branches, or to remain stock-still in a posture for hours on end. Tarsiers differ from the lorisids in having two sets of grooming claws on their feet. They have long, slender fingers, which they can move independently.

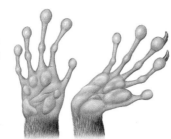

HANDS **FEET**
TARSIER

THE FUR

is soft and thick, even woolly, and generally paler on the underside. Scent glands lie beneath the fur on the head and neck and around the sexual organs.

FACT FILE:
LESSER GALAGO

CLASSIFICATION

GENUS: *GALAGO*
SPECIES: *SENEGALENSIS*

SIZE

HEAD-BODY LENGTH: **6.3–6.7** IN (16–17 CM)
TAIL LENGTH: **9–10** IN (23–25 CM)
WEIGHT: **5–7** OZ (150–200 G)
WEIGHT AT BIRTH: **0.4–0.5** OZ (12–15 G)

COLORATION

PALE GRAY TO BLUISH GRAY FUR, OFTEN BROWN OR YELLOW ON ARMS AND THIGHS
UNDERSIDE GENERALLY PALER
DARK PATCHES AROUND EYES AND WHITE BRIDGE OF NOSE

FEATURES

LARGE, ROUND EYES, FACING FORWARD AND SET CLOSE TOGETHER
PROMINENT BATLIKE EARS
ROUNDED HEAD AND SHORT SNOUT
LONG HIND LIMBS
LONG, BUSHY TAIL

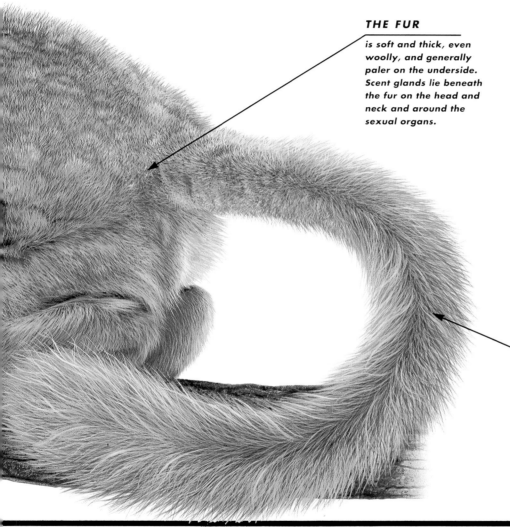

THE TAIL

is long and luxuriantly furred. It serves as a balancing device during leaps, but is not capable of grasping.

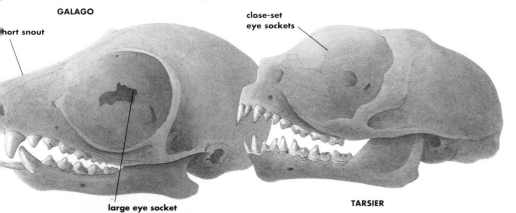

GALAGO
short snout
close-set eye sockets
large eye socket
TARSIER

TOOTH-COMB
The peglike incisors in the galago's lower jaw form a special "tooth-comb." This comb has two purposes: it is raked over the fur during grooming to remove rough debris and tangled hair, and it is also used to scoop gum from fissures in tree bark. A second comblike structure—this time a fleshy outgrowth of the tongue—is used to clean the tooth-comb.

tooth-comb   canines
molars

Main illustration Steve Kingston

LEAPERS AND CREEPERS

GALAGOS, POTTOS, LORISES, AND TARSIERS ALL SPEND THEIR NIGHTS ROAMING VEGETATION IN SEARCH OF FOOD, BUT THEY CERTAINLY DO NOT ALL GO ABOUT IT AT THE SAME PACE

Resting in their hiding places while the sun is up, lorisids and tarsiers start their daily activities as dusk approaches in their tropical homes. They stir about half an hour before sundown, with yawns and the stretching of limbs. Still remaining secure amid dense foliage or in tree holes, they start to busy themselves cleaning their fur. Both the toilet claws and, in lorisids, the special tooth-comb are put to good use in grooming out bits of debris and separating tangled hairs.

Galagos eventually move away from their sleeping places several minutes before full darkness, giving any quiet human observers a brief chance to see them in action before the light fails completely. Pottos are more cautious, waiting until all is dark before they emerge from hiding.

FOREST TREK

Though groups of galagos will happily sleep together through the day, often in family groups, their nocturnal activity is almost always solitary. Typically a galago will move away from the rest area along a regularly used path toward a chosen

> ALLEN'S GALAGO, WHICH NESTS IN TREE HOLES, CHECKS THE LIGHT LEVEL OUTSIDE BEFORE EMERGING AT DUSK

foraging site. For the species that occur in wooded savanna, known collectively as lesser and greater galagos, this may involve a rapid journey of running or hopping along branches, leaps across manageable gaps, and bouts of running or hopping over the ground when gaps between trees are too large. When they reach their foraging sites, galagos busy themselves in an agile search over trunks, branches, and twigs for insects and other small prey, fruit,

seeds, flowers, or gum. Constantly twitching and furling their ears and staring around with their fixed round eyes, they are ever alert for prey as well as for danger.

Tarsiers are similarly ever alert when exposed, ears waving back and forth and head swinging to turn the great soup-plate eyes toward the direction of any unexpected sound. Tarsiers are not so adept at clambering around branches as the galagos, and spend much of their time clinging to vertical surfaces from which they scan the surroundings for prey. Their agility, however, is revealed in dramatic fashion when they pounce on a victim or launch themselves several feet through the air to another perch to escape danger.

In striking contrast, the pottos and lorises are devoted to slow-motion behavior. Gripping branches with their hands and feet, they creep along so

A slow loris (above) *demonstrates its ability to grip branches firmly and hang effortlessly for hours.*

I. & L. Beames/Ardea

Kenneth W. Fink/Ardea

NIGHT SIGHTS

The round eyes of the lorisids and tarsiers are so sensitive to light that they enable the animals to see objects clearly and make precise leaps on all but the darkest nights. Enormous pupils gather as much light in as possible and, in the lorisids, once the incoming light has passed and stimulated the retina it is bounced back out again by a reflective layer called the tapetum. This is the brilliant eye reflection seen when a lorisid is caught in torchlight. The tapetum is not present in tarsiers, but they compensate by having eyes so large they dominate the shape of the head, making the skull broader than it is long.

slowly, smoothly, and silently that they can stalk insects and other prey for minutes, quite unnoticed, until they are close enough to strike. But more importantly, this form of "cryptic locomotion" makes it extremely difficult for predators to detect them whether they are stalking prey or eating fruit and gum. Though they never leap, they show a different form of acrobatics, since they are able to hang upside down from branches and freeze motionless for long minutes or even hours in awkward postures without suffering from a cramp.

MIDNIGHT FESTIVITIES

Lorisids and tarsiers can spend most of the night foraging, but usually take a rest when they are full, often in the middle of the night. Breaks from feeding also occur for social reasons. Galagos, for example, meet up with one another occasionally, especially at the sites where they lick the sticky sap from gum trees, and often spend time grooming one another or playing. But unfamiliar individuals are likely to elicit more aggressive responses. Lorisids and tarsiers also spend some of their waking hours leaving scent marks and engaging in bouts of calling to proclaim their territories and communicate with their neighbors or associates.

As soon as their extraordinary eyes detect a remote hint of dawn, lorisids and tarsiers start to return to their refuges, meeting up again with any sleeping partners as they approach. Once they have settled down to sleep, they will only stir in daylight if disturbed or threatened. ∎

The extraordinary eyes of a Philippine tarsier gaze into the night, intent on spotting insect prey.

HABITATS

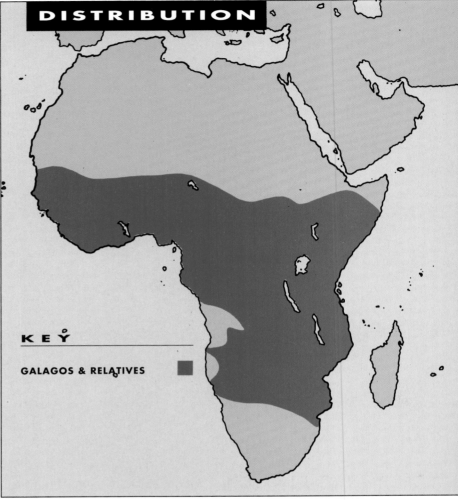

DISTRIBUTION

KEY

GALAGOS & RELATIVES ■

Galagos, pottos, lorises, and tarsiers are all adapted for lives spent sheltering in, and traveling around, trees and shrubs in the tropics. But between them, the various species show preferences for different types of habitat.

Some of the most elusive lorisids are virtually confined to closed-canopy primary rain forest, among them the needle-clawed galagos and the potto. Primary forests are those that have not been altered at all by man. Others prefer more open or modified habitats, though their habits still make them hard to find. Various races of the slender loris are associated with different forms of forest and woodland in India, including monsoon forests that shed much of their foliage in the dry season, and there is an especially thick-furred race that occupies cool, mountain forests in central Sri Lanka. The angwantibo of Africa is closely associated with natural forest clearings, where tree falls have opened up the canopy and there is plenty of dense undergrowth.

Tarsiers occupy a range of forest types in island southeast Asia, including primary rain forest, mangrove swamp, and thick scrub. The western tarsier seems to like secondary rain forest—that is, forest that has been partially cleared in the past by man and is in the process of regeneration. Compared with primary rain forest, such forest is characterized by

Nick Gordon/Survival Anglia

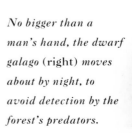

Pottos (left) inhabit the moist forests of equatorial Africa, where they share their home with the galagos.

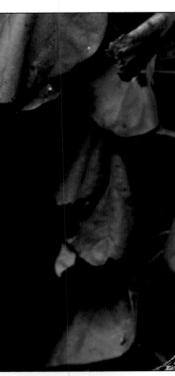

No bigger than a man's hand, the dwarf galago (right) moves about by night, to avoid detection by the forest's predators.

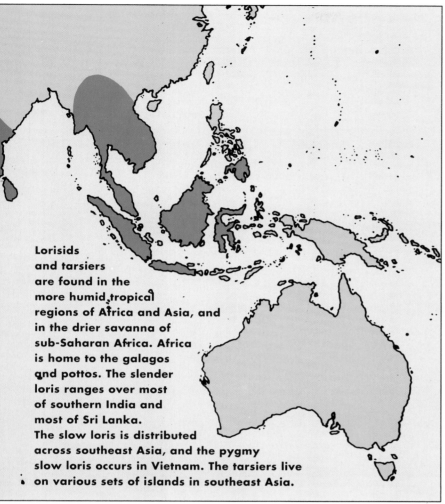

Lorisids
and tarsiers
are found in the
more humid tropical
regions of Africa and Asia, and
in the drier savanna of
sub-Saharan Africa. Africa
is home to the galagos
and pottos. The slender
loris ranges over most
of southern India and
most of Sri Lanka.
The slow loris is distributed
across southeast Asia, and the pygmy
slow loris occurs in Vietnam. The tarsiers live
on various sets of islands in southeast Asia.

narrower, more closely spaced tree trunks. Similar habitats are provided by commercial plantations, and the western tarsier colonizes these, too.

Some widespread species of lorisids do not depend on forests and have consequently become more conspicuous. The lesser and the greater galagos of Africa—there are at least two species of both—are equally if not more at home in wooded savanna and dry bush, so long as there are enough trees or thickets in which they can take refuge and for them to avoid spending too much time crossing spaces at ground level. Of all the lorisids, these species are the most commonly seen. For lesser galagos, densities of up to 520 per square mile have been recorded in woodland savanna regions of East Africa, and in dense acacia thickets in South Africa the figure can reach 1,300. They can move easily among dense thorns, forbidding to most other mammals, and their orange eyes flash in car headlights on many an acacia-lined bush road.

These two groups of galagos are particularly hardy and adaptable compared to most other lorisids. Greater bush babies colonize pine, eucalyptus, and coffee plantations, and even appear in wooded suburban gardens. Their well-known wailing calls are probably the reason galagos gained their nickname of bush babies.

FINDING A NICHE

As well as occupying differing wooded habitats, lorisids and tarsiers also utilize habitats in different ways. Some species remain high up almost all of

Terry Mayes/Planet Earth Pictures

KEY FACTS

● With a head-and-body length of just 4.7 in (12 cm), dwarf galagos are among the world's smallest primates.

● Both galagos and tarsiers can leap several yards between the branches of trees. Tarsiers in particular can make giant leaps with seemingly little effort—jumps covering gaps of 20 ft (6 m) have been recorded. Lesser galagos can make upward leaps of up to 6.5 ft (2 m).

● Though they spend most of their time moving very slowly, pottos and lorises can sustain a faster pace for brief periods if they are forced to cross exposed passageways.

● Lorisids occasionally engage in serious fights if threat displays fail to sooth disputes. Greater galagos have been seen tumbling to the ground locked in combat.

● When fully extended, the powerful hind limbs of a tarsier reach almost twice the length of the animal's head and torso.

the time, in the dense tree crowns. This is the realm of the potto, which moves from outspreading branch to branch in the closed canopy searching for fruit and rarely descending to the floor. Tarsiers, on the other hand, spend much of their active time clinging to the lower portions of tree trunks, supported by their long fingers and bracing with the tail. Needle-clawed galagos are also adept at grasping trunks. Ridges in the center of their nails extend to form clawlike projections with which the animals can grip trunks too wide and smooth for other galagos.

Still other species live in the understory and in shrubs close to the ground. The angwantibo is the most restricted to this level. Adapted for clambering in dense vegetation over narrow stems and vines, it cannot climb trunks and larger branches and rarely crosses open ground.

Sleeping places also vary among the different species. Preferred sites for galagos and tarsiers may be within dense clumps of foliage, in the fork of a branch, in a tree cavity, or in an abandoned bird's nest. Some galago family groups build nests of leaves in these places. Pottos and lorises curl up hidden in dense foliage either in the understory or up in the canopy depending on where they feel most at home.

K. & K. Ammann/Planet Earth Pictures. Inset Ron Austin/Oxford Scientific Films

FOCUS ON

THE CONGO RAIN FOREST

Lorisids live in the rain forests of Africa and Asia. However, more species occur together in the equatorial rain forest of central Africa than in any other ecosystem. Here can be found dwarf galagos, needle-clawed galagos, Allen's galagos, and pottos, including angwantibos. The Congo rain forest is the most extensive of the regions of primary forest in Africa. A broad block of greenery 950 miles (1,500 km) long and 500 miles (800 km) wide around the mighty River Congo, it is watered by heavy rain for most of the year and bathed in tropical heat. There are several hundred tree species, among them ebony and mahogany, and some 400 types of orchid. Everywhere among the trees smaller plants take hold, among them ferns, lichens, figs, creepers, and vines. This mass of vegetation provides food and refuge for a fittingly diverse fauna.

The forest has no fewer than 700 species of ants. Even more numerous are beetles, which include the 4 in (10 cm) goliath beetle. Indeed, the African rain forest has more than its fair share of giants, including the largest land snail and the largest frog, along with outsized mantids, centipedes, millipedes, and flatworms. Other spectacular inhabitants include vipers, chameleons, hornbills, forest kingfishers, monkeys, leopards, and forest elephants.

RAIN FOREST LAYERS

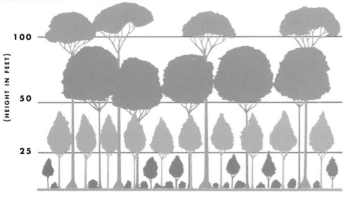

(HEIGHT IN FEET)

100

50

25

Rain forests comprise a number of vertical layers. The bulk of foliage is in the canopy. Above this stand a few very tall "emergent" trees, while directly below lies an "understory" of smaller trees with narrow crowns, palms, and shrubs. The ground cover of seedlings, herbs, and shade-tolerant plants is fairly sparse.

Differences in the ways in which animals utilize the same habitat for food and shelter make it easier for more than one species to live together without undue competition. This so-called "niche separation" is most marked in the rain forests of central Africa, where up to four species of galago may happily coexist—along with the potto and the angwantibo. Demidoff's dwarf galago, for example, generally keeps to the leafy cover of the tree crowns, while Allen's galago is largely active among ground vegetation. ∎

NEIGHBORS

The rain forests of central Africa are not as rich in species as those of Asia and South America, but nevertheless are home to a bewildering range of wild animals and luxuriant plant growth.

AFRICAN CROCODILE

Forest rivers are home for the dwarf crocodile, which has suffered greatly from hunting for its hide.

HIPPO

The hippo is primarily a savanna animal, but can be found in the Congo along rivers in forest clearings.

Illustrations Joanne Cowne/Cobra & Genet Edwina Goldstone

Rain forests in central Africa stretch several degrees north and south of the Equator, from Zaire, through the Congo, west to the Gabon coast. A narrower belt of rain forest continues, though patchily, along coastal West Africa as far as Sierra Leone.

GABON

CONGO

ZAIRE

Equator

Atlantic Ocean

ANGOLA

RAIN FOREST

FOREST HOG

The giant forest hog is the largest of the wild pigs. It roams around in family groups of up to twelve.

AFRICAN FISH EAGLE

This eagle often perches on a branch over a forest pool, and swoops to snatch fish with its fearsome talons.

COBRA

Known by their hooded head and deadly bite, cobras are common across much of Africa.

MANDRILL

The rain forest is home to the mandrill, its biggest and most bizarre monkey, with its vivid face mask.

GENET

A relative of the mongoose, the genet silently stalks its prey among the branches of rain-forest trees.

LOCOMOTION

Lorises and pottos can make brief rapid movements, but they cannot leap. Instead, they creep along branches with absolute poise and smoothness, which makes them extremely difficult to detect. Flexible limb joints and digits that close in a vicelike grip enable them to move deliberately, hand over hand and foot over foot, even while dangling beneath a horizontal branch.

Tarsiers are built for rather different movement. Their powerful hind limbs are extremely long. By retracting and then springing the leg muscles into extension, a tarsier can leap across gaps, twisting its body around in midleap if necessary so that it lands front first. Tarsiers can also leap on flat surfaces, as well as run, hop, and climb.

Needle-clawed galagos can leap expertly. Springing from a trunk, they swing the tail up to rotate the body into an all-fours landing position on a trunk up to 18 ft (5.5 m) away. Lesser galagos often leap with their arms raised. Allen's galago is highly agile in leaping between thin trunks. It can cover a distance of 40 ft (12 m) in five seconds with a series of quick-fire leaps.

Dwarf galagos can race along thin vines, and spring across short gaps with almost no loss of height. Greater galagos are better runners and walkers than leapers. On branches they move rather like monkeys, while on the ground they either hop on their hind limbs or run with their haunches and tail raised. ∎

BOUNDERS

Galagos (above) *are agile climbers, runners, and jumpers in the trees. Many of them can leap long distances, hang under branches, and move headfirst or tail-first on tree trunks.*

SIGHT

FROZEN IN FEAR

If it detects the slightest disturbance, a loris (*right*) or a potto will freeze, with its eyes fixed upon the source of interest. With uncanny muscular discipline, the animal can remain stock-still for hours until it once more feels safe. Special circulatory systems in the limbs make sure that these parts receive a good blood supply, preventing muscle fatigue. Freezing, combined with the snail's-pace locomotion, are good ways of avoiding detection by predators, but they depend on lorises and pottos keeping within the concealment of thick vegetation.

Joe Blossom/NHPA

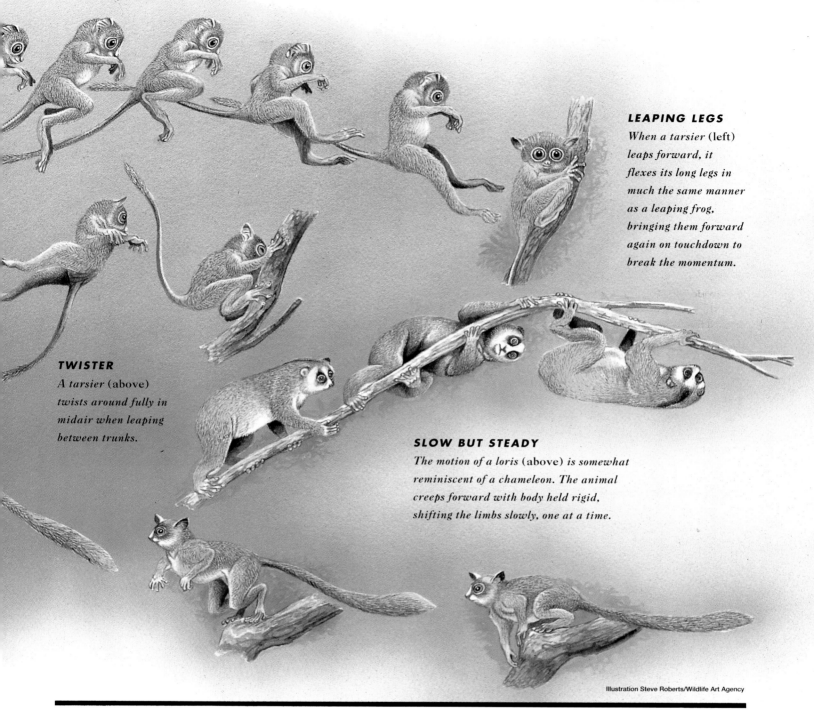

LEAPING LEGS

When a tarsier (left) leaps forward, it flexes its long legs in much the same manner as a leaping frog, bringing them forward again on touchdown to break the momentum.

TWISTER

A tarsier (above) twists around fully in midair when leaping between trunks.

SLOW BUT STEADY

The motion of a loris (above) is somewhat reminiscent of a chameleon. The animal creeps forward with body held rigid, shifting the limbs slowly, one at a time.

Illustration Steve Roberts/Wildlife Art Agency

DEFENSIVE POSTURES

Should an enemy detect it, a potto is in trouble; unlike a galago, it cannot leap away to safety. It has little choice but to stand ground, but this is something at which it is adept. Turning toward the aggressor, the potto seizes the branch, lowers its head, and presents its nape. On the back of the potto's neck, thick fur and skin cover a row of bony knobs on the spine between the shoulder blades. Altogether this acts like a shield against bites and blows. If the predator comes close, the potto suddenly lurches forward, often butting with its shield or lifting its head and biting hard.

    The angwantibo has no such shield, and its defense method is bizarre. If caught near the ground, it rolls into a ball, with its head tucked between its chest and one arm. Confused predators probing further may suddenly find a bite directed at their snout from the angwantibo's armpit. If this does not deter them, the violent recoil of the aggressor will tend to throw the angwantibo to safety.

B/W illustrations Evi Antoniou

745

FOOD AND FEEDING

Sleeping aside, the most time-consuming activity of galagos, pottos, lorises, and tarsiers is the nightly search for food. Tarsiers are among the few primates that subsist virtually exclusively on animal food. The lorisids eat mainly insects and plant matter, in varied proportions according to body size. In general, the larger animals rely more on vegetation, to provide bulk. Lorisids are rare among animals in that they can digest gum—the sticky substance exuded from trees to patch up wounds in the bark.

Galagos use their hands to catch insects. Sensing a beetle, a grasshopper, or a moth nearby, the galago tracks its victim largely by sound before making a lightning pounce with one or both hands and instantly transferring the creature to its mouth where it first bites the head. At the moment of capture it closes its eyes and retracts its ears to prevent damage from flailing body parts. Dwarf galagos are so skilled at this that they can snatch gnats from

PINNING DOWN PREY

The tarsier's long fingers act like a cage so that even when a swift insect reacts in the last split second, it is likely to be caught.

A slow loris (above) catches live prey, such as this leaf-mimicking insect, by stealing up on it incredibly slowly.

PREY

Galagos and their relatives supplement a diet of plant matter with a range of invertebrate prey. Lorises and pottos in particular will readily eat insects that would repel or even poison most other mammals.

MOTHS

GRASSHOPPERS

the air. The larger species of galago that require more plant food tend to specialize on certain types. Hence Allen's galago forages largely for fallen fruit, while the needle-clawed galago mostly searches trunks for fresh gum, visiting up to a hundred sites every hour.

STALE GUM AND BEETLES

Lorises and pottos also feed on fruit and gum, especially the larger species—the slow loris and the potto. The potto crawls through the tree canopy, eating not just soft fruit and fresh gum, but also the tough-skinned fruit and hard, stale lumps of gum that galagos cannot manage. Lorises and pottos also seize and devour invertebrates that interest few other animals. These include ants, poisonous spiders, snails, slugs, foul-smelling beetles, and noxious larvae—creatures that are either slow-moving or unpalatable and are therefore easy for a stealthy animal to catch. The angwantibo happily feeds on caterpillars with irritant hairs. Holding the head in

---

THERE ARE REPORTS OF GALAGOS CATCHING SMALL VERTEBRATES, BUT THIS APPEARS TO BE RARE IN THE WILD

---

its teeth, it first rubs a caterpillar to remove some of the hairs before tucking in. Though their stealthy movement does allow them to sneak up on some more palatable but more active prey, including lizards and nesting birds, lorises and pottos appear to move the way they do more for reasons of safety than for gathering food.

Tarsiers catch the bulk of their victims by pinpointing their position using sound and sight, and then pinning them down with a deft leap. Using one or both hands to hold prey in place, either on the ground or on a branch, a tarsier then bites it swiftly to immobilize it. Common prey includes large insects, such as grasshoppers, beetles, and cockroaches, supplemented occasionally with scorpions, lizards, birds, bats, and even poisonous snakes. Victims are usually carried back in the mouth to a perch and held in one hand while they are devoured. ■

inSIGHT

RETRO-VISION

When scanning the surroundings for prey with its ears and eyes, a tarsier constantly moves its head. Since the animal's huge eyes face forward their fields of vision overlap, and therefore provide excellent stereoscopic vision; this enables the animal to judge leaps to perfection. However, the eyes are so immobile in their sockets that if the tarsier is to look around it is obliged to rotate its head as an owl does.

But also like an owl, it has the ability to twist its head all the way back through 180 degrees. This enables the tarsier to peer directly behind without changing body posture—and therefore with the minimum of movement that might alert either prey or enemies.

Simon Turvey/Wildlife Art Agency

AMBUSH BABIES

Galagos catch insects and other prey either by leaping and grabbing them as they appear or by creeping up first. Some galagos can even snatch insects from the air, tracking them by sound.

GNATS

SHIELDBUGS

LEAFHOPPERS

Prey illustrations Evi Antoniou

SOCIAL STRUCTURE

Unlike many other primates, galagos, pottos, lorises, and tarsiers are more or less solitary creatures when out foraging. But that does not mean they are unconcerned with social contact. For animals that can hear and smell so well, there is plenty of scope for distance communication through the forest, whether the motives are territorial, sexual, alarm-raising, or simply the need to keep in touch through the darkness.

Tarsiers are renowned for their high-pitched calls, some of which are probably beyond the range of human hearing. Male and female spectral tarsiers keep in contact while foraging with delightful duets, in which each sex returns its call in a distinctive voice. In this species, males and females appear to form stable bonds, and together defend a territory from intruders, marking it out with urine and scent from chest glands. They tolerate young female offspring within their range but juvenile male young have to disperse once they can fend for themselves. Western tarsiers do not pair up so readily, although the ranges of males and females frequently overlap. A typical home range might cover an area of 2.5 acres (one hectare).

Though they use calls when encountering one another at close range, lorises and pottos rely rather less on vocal communication. For animals that use concealment to evade predators, frequent bouts of loud calling would be counterproductive. But they make up for this with scent. Both the slow loris and the potto have a strong, currylike body odor, and all species copiously scent mark their territories. The potto frequently places its rear end against a branch and shuffles forward a short way, leaving a trail of urine. Pottos also mark objects and one another—especially when breeding—with scent from glands near their sexual organs. Scent deposits are generally sufficient to regulate the spacing of individuals in the forest and also serve as communication between neighbors. Male pottos tend to have bigger territories, up to 16 acres (40 hectares) in some cases, which often overlap the territories of several females.

SOCIAL GALAGOS

Galagos are the most sociable of the lorisids. Groups of them often sleep together and their encounters during foraging are more frequent. Sleeping groups usually consist of a mother with female offspring of different ages and their dependent young, sometimes with an adult male present. Members of the group go their separate ways when foraging, each female keeping to her established home range, but these ranges overlap extensively and converge on the sleeping sites. Most hostile interactions are reserved for unrelated females from areas adjacent to the group area.

Female offspring, therefore, tend to remain fairly close to where they were born, but male galagos

URINE-WASHING IN GALAGOS

For many galagos the most frequent form of scent marking involves the unusual behavior known as "urine-washing." Lesser galagos, for example, indulge in this ritual once or twice every hour when out foraging, and it spreads the message of their presence wherever they go. One side at a time, they raise both the hand and foot off the branch and urinate into the cupped hand. They then use the hand to rub the sole of the raised foot. The action is then repeated with the other hand and foot. This procedure takes just a few seconds but it serves to transfer the scent of urine wherever the galago subsequently travels. It may be that urine-washing also gives the animals a better grip by moistening the palms and soles. As well as urine-washing, galagos rub scent from their faces or chests on objects, as well as depositing trails of urine directly onto supports in a similar way to the potto.

Illustration Robin Budden/Wildlife Art Agency

disperse when they reach breeding age. After a period of wandering, they tend to establish territories on the periphery of female groups, often in close company with other males of a similar age. Their aspiration is one day to supplant an established dominant male. Such males hold extensive territories, up to 50 acres (20 hectares) in the case of Allen's galago, often centered on a female group and so overlapping with the home ranges of as many as eight females. The central male will try to maintain social and sexual bonds with these females by visiting each every night or two and engaging in social grooming. Every now and again his status is challenged by one of the peripheral males, and if threat postures with ears spread and teeth bared are not enough to settle the rivalry, wrestling and biting fights may ensue.

To mark territories and leave contact messages, galagos make use of urine and other scent secretions, but they also call. Even within species, calling in galagos is both complex and variable, making it hard to define meanings for individual sounds, but generally speaking the loudest wails, croaks, barks, and squeals are used to advertise territories and establish contact at a distance. For short-distance communication, there are quieter croaks, squeaks, clicks, spits, grunts, and growls. These may initiate gatherings, maintain contact between mother and infant, indicate courtship or aggression, or signify alarm or distress. ∎

Lesser galagos (below) defend their territory against neighboring groups or young single males.

LIFE CYCLE

For the savanna-dwelling species of galago, the climate is markedly seasonal; so the lesser and the greater galagos time mating so that births take place in the wet season. During this period, a female lesser galago gives birth to up to two litters, each with one to three young. The rain forest galagos, along with the pottos, lorises, and tarsiers, have a less-precise breeding season in keeping with their more stable climate, yet birth peaks tend to coincide with certain months when food is most abundant. As in many rain-forest mammals, a single young is the norm.

COURTING COUPLES

Reproductive behavior is preceded by acts of courtship, which vary considerably in vigor. In the western tarsier it generally involves a good deal of chasing and calling. In galagos there are ritual stages of chasing, sniffing, facial licking, and long periods of mutual grooming that build up the pair

MATING

When ready for mating, a female lesser galago allows the male she has already court-ed to grasp her waist from behind and mount. Copulation lasts for several minutes at a time.

PIGGYBACK

After the initial period in the nest, the mother takes her young out every night, "parking" them on a branch while she feeds in one tree before moving them on to the next.

Alain Compost/Bruce Coleman Ltd.

A newborn loris is remarkably agile, and its fingers possess a tenacious grip. Nevertheless, it will be several months before it is brave enough to venture far from its mother. Until that time, it spends many a night clinging to her fur as she feeds (left).

GROWING UP

The life of a lesser galago

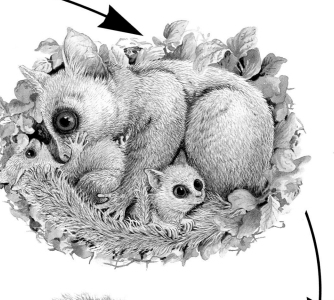

HELPLESS YOUNG

In lesser galagos, there are usually two young born in a litter (left). *Their eyes are open from birth, but they are unable to move purposefully about the nest until a few days have passed.*

LESSER GALAGO	WESTERN TARSIER
BREEDING: USUALLY 2 BREEDING PERIODS PER YEAR	**BREEDING:** ANY TIME OF THE YEAR, BUT BIRTHS PEAK IN FEBRUARY–APRIL
GESTATION: 4 MONTHS	**GESTATION:** 6 MONTHS
LITTER SIZE: 1–3	**LITTER SIZE:** 1
WEIGHT AT BIRTH: 12–15 G (0.4–0.5 oz)	**WEIGHT AT BIRTH:** 20–30 G (0.7–1 oz)
EYES OPEN: AT BIRTH	**EYES OPEN:** AT BIRTH
WEANING: 10–11 WEEKS	**WEANING:** 8 WEEKS
SEXUAL MATURITY: 10 MONTHS	**SEXUAL MATURITY:** 1 YEAR
LONGEVITY: UP TO 15 YEARS IN CAPTIVITY	**LONGEVITY:** 8–12 YEARS

bond. This may take place several days before the female is physically ready to mate. In the potto, on the other hand, there is little close contact at all prior to mating.

A HEAD START IN LIFE

Gestation periods can be long for such small mammals, up to six months in the case of the tarsiers. But the advantage is that the newborn young are quite well developed and quickly begin to find their way around. An angwantibo gives birth on a branch, and the newborn must immediately climb up and cling to its mother's belly fur, where it will

---

AT ONE DAY OLD A TARSIER CAN CLIMB AROUND A LITTLE, AND WEIGHS ALMOST A QUARTER OF ITS MOTHER'S WEIGHT

---

remain for several days. As soon as a slow loris is born it can cling firmly to thin branches. Newborn galagos are less precocious. Their eyes are only half-opened, and they can only crawl about awkwardly. Accordingly they are born in secure leaf nests or in tree hollows.

In all species, within a few days the young can cling tightly enough to accompany the mother while foraging, although she "parks" it each night (see box). By ten days, the young is becoming ever more mobile in the nest. It can climb, stand, jump, and wrestle. In the greater and needle-clawed galagos, the mother is big enough to carry an infant on her back all the time while foraging and does so when it is aged about four weeks. The same applies to the lorises and pottos.

By about six weeks the young of all species of lorisids and tarsiers have learned to move about on their own, though they keep close to their parent, and are learning to find palatable food for themselves. Weaning is shortly thereafter. After several months of foraging within its mother's range, the offspring approaches adult weight. ∎

Illustrations Wendy Bramell/Wildlife Art Agency

AIR CARGO

Should predators threaten the nest, the protective mother is fully prepared to carry the young in her mouth (above), *even when leaping dramatically between branches.*

As soon as an infant lorisid or tarsier can grip tightly, its mother takes it out at night and "parks" it while foraging. At each feeding site she places the young on a thin branch, to which it instinctively grips, while she busies herself nearby. In this manner she can keep an eye on the young, which is so tiny that it is unlikely to be detected by predators. But even then, the infant can make a last-ditch escape attempt by letting go and dropping to the ground.

CLINGING TO EXISTENCE

CONCEALMENT WITHIN THE CLOAK OF DARKNESS HELPS LORISIDS AND TARSIERS AVOID MANY HAZARDS, BOTH NATURAL AND HUMAN-INDUCED, BUT THE PROTECTION NOCTURNAL LIFE AFFORDS IS FAR FROM TOTAL

A slender loris making its way ponderously along a branch in full daylight would not last long. Lethargic and lightweight, it would be exposed to predation from a whole range of forest hunters. A lesser galago, even though it can run and leap through thickets, would be fairly easy meat for a sharp-eyed hawk or eagle striking from above if it foraged by day. And an infant clinging immobile to a stem would be the easiest possible meal for the smallest climbing carnivore.

It is darkness that makes the various defense strategies of cryptic movement, leaping ability, and immobility work for these animals. It makes them harder to detect and makes it easier for them to escape when detected. With senses tuned to making the most of moonlight or starlight, as well as of the faintest sound or smell, galagos, pottos, lorises, and tarsiers have a good chance of noting danger before it notes them.

NATURAL THREATS

Even so, threats to the survival of lorisids and tarsiers persist. There are plenty of predatory animals adapted for nocturnal life, too. Owls are a major enemy of the diminutive species—the smaller galagos, the tarsiers, and the slender lorises. Even a potto or a greater galagos can be picked off by one of the powerful eagle owls that range across Africa. The genet, a climbing cat-like carnivore related to the mongoose, is a threat for arboreal galagos, particularly on the darkest nights when vision is blanked out. The genet may also attack pottos, and its cousin, the palm civet, has been observed doing so—although it has also been seen thrown off a branch by the potto's vigorous counterattack.

Allen's galago and the angwantibo, which forage close to the ground level, are vulnerable to a range of ground-based predators, including the golden cat and the leopard. Greater galagos crossing the ground between trees on the savanna are easy for leopards and hyenas to catch. All lorisids and tarsiers face the threat of snakes sneaking up on them, whether at night or while they are resting by day. Pythons are large enough to tackle the biggest species, and venomous snakes can also be a danger to some. Lesser galagos provide an important share of the diet of the black mamba.

Like all its relatives, the greater galago (above) *is threatened by the deforestation of its habitat.*

Gerald Cubbitt/Bruce Coleman Ltd.

Steve Turner/Oxford Scientific Films

As well as from hunting animals, lorisids and tarsiers face the threat from organisms of a rather different kind—a threat that no amount of concealment can counter. Like all creatures they are at risk from parasites, especially from intestinal worms, and from diseases, some of which, as primates, they share with humans. Populations of galagos are known to be capable of harboring yellow fever, which could be transferred via mosquitoes to people and vice versa. A serious outbreak of yellow fever in Sudan in 1940 may have been linked with the high population of lesser galagos in the area of the epidemic.

LOGGING ON THE ISLANDS OF SULAWESI AND BORNEO CLAIMS THE LIVES OF TENS OF THOUSANDS OF TARSIERS EVERY YEAR

Lesser and greater galagos are also vulnerable to bushfires in their savanna habitat. Fires sweeping through dry vegetation can consume them directly or force the animals to flee across open ground where they are easy prey for opportunist predators. Bushfires can occur naturally, but many are the result of human actions—deliberate setting of fires or the alteration of habitats causing them to become more fire prone. Against fire, of course, the night once again provides no refuge. This is the case with most human-induced threats to lorisids and tarsiers, the most serious of which is the destruction of tropical forest habitats.

FOREST CLEARANCE

Across Africa and Asia, tropical forests have been cleared or degraded at an alarming rate during the present century, reducing the ranges and populations of all the forest-dwelling species. Both the slender loris and the slow loris have declined wherever forest cover has been cleared in tropical Asia. The last two decades, for example, have seen the slow loris disappear from most of its former range in Bangladesh and Peninsular Malaysia. The western tarsier has lost much of its former forest to widespread logging and land clearance in Indonesia, and deforestation has removed most of the potto's habitat in the west of Africa.

Species and subspecies with restricted ranges are those of most conservation concern. Thomas's galago and the Zanzibar galago, both species that have a fragmented distribution across the forest patches in East Africa, are in danger because their homes can easily be swallowed up

A slender loris in the forests of southern India, where trees are felled for fuelwood.

LORISIDS AND TARSIERS IN DANGER

THE INTERNATIONAL UNION FOR THE CONSERVATION OF NATURE (IUCN) LISTS THE FOLLOWING SPECIES OF LORISID AND TARSIER IN ITS 1994 *RED DATA BOOK* OF THREATENED ANIMALS:

PHILIPPINE TARSIER	ENDANGERED
GOLDEN POTTO	VULNERABLE
PYGMY SLOW LORIS	VULNERABLE
ZANZIBAR GALAGO	VULNERABLE
EASTERN NEEDLE-CLAWED GALAGO	VULNERABLE
LESSER SPECTRAL TARSIER	INDETERMINATE
SPECTRAL TARSIER	INSUFFICIENTLY KNOWN
THOMAS'S GALAGOY	INSUFFICIENTLY KNOWN

As well as destroying habitats, people create other environmental hazards for lorisids and tarsiers. Western tarsiers have been able to colonize commercial plantations, but sometimes with tragic consequences as pesticides applied to the crops accumulate in their bodies via their insect food. Pottos end up electrocuted as they take a grip on high-tension cables, or are run over as they try to cross the rift in a forest created by a road.

HUNTING AND TRADE

Nocturnal secrecy, combined with small body size, has spared lorisids and tarsiers to a large extent from the pressures of being hunted by people for their meat—pressures that afflict some populations of monkeys and other mammals. However, there is a history of hunting lorises in India and Indonesia for the use of body parts in traditional medicine. Until recently, a considerable number of slender lorises were captured to be used as laboratory animals in biomedical experiments.

Tarsiers are sometimes caught and sold for pets in Borneo, but it seems they rarely survive for long. The same goes for galagos, lorises, and pottos, especially if they are taken as pets to climates very different from their own. Sadly, their death often leads to the bereaved and distraught "owner" seeking a replacement, and thereby continuing to fuel the trade. ∎

by land clearance. Forest refuges along the coast of Kenya and Tanzania are particularly vulnerable to land development and tree cutting for firewood and timber. The pygmy slow loris has undoubtedly suffered from devastation brought to its forest home in Vietnam and neighboring countries by modern warfare. Deforestation threatens the Philippine tarsier in all the places it inhabits—three areas on the heavily populated island of Mindanao, and the islands of Samar, Leyte, Dinagat, and Siargao Bohol.

A slow loris in Bangkok's markets, where wild species of all description are sold —whether or not they are legally protected.

ALONGSIDE MAN

MYTH AND MAGIC

Not surprisingly, these wide-eyed creatures of the night have found their way into the folklore of peoples in Africa and Asia. Some African proverbs, for example, glorify the potto for its strong grip, while Allen's galago is said by some to warn of approaching leopards in the forest. Both are based on truth—the latter because this undergrowth-dwelling galago habitually raises an alarm call when it senses danger. Among some of the former head-hunting tribes of Borneo, the tarsier possessed special symbolism because of the belief that its head was loose—a myth based on the animal's remarkably flexible neck.

In some regions, lorisids and tarsiers have traditionally been caught for food or to keep as pets, and both greater and lesser galagos are sometimes caught for their meat.

C. B. Frith/Bruce Coleman Ltd.

INTO THE FUTURE

The long-term future of galagos, pottos, lorises, and tarsiers depends very much on whether deforestation pressures rise or wane in Africa and Asia in coming decades. Many isolated populations of lorisids and tarsiers are now being squeezed from much of their former ranges.

Even those populations in the remotest tracts of the Congo rain forest may one day find their habitat threatened by deforestation. On the savanna, pressures on trees and shrubs from livestock overcrowding and fuelwood gathering will likewise threaten the habitat of lesser and greater galagos.

The most important way to ensure that at least some suitable habitat remains for these animals is to designate national parks and preserves and protect environments. Existing protected areas already contain populations of most species. Key refuges for tarsiers, for example, include Kinabalu National

PREDICTION

A SHORTFALL OF INFORMATION

Predictions are hampered by uncertainty—not just over the future pace of deforestation, but also by the fact that so little is known about these animals. Data from present studies will probably disclose more areas where they occur, and also reveal new populations and species that must be listed as endangered.

Park in Sabah, Malaysia, for the western tarsier, and Tangkoko Batuangas Reserve in Sulawesi, Indonesia, for the spectral tarsier. The Philippine tarsier, however, which is the most seriously threatened species, is not yet benefiting from any park or preserve.

Though hunting and collecting of lorisids and tarsiers is not a great problem overall, it becomes a more significant threat whenever wild populations dwindle alarmingly. Some protective legislation is already in place: Several of the species, including both types of slow loris, are covered by international trade controls. Domestic laws were passed in 1931 in Indonesia to protect—at least on paper—the western tarsier from hunting. The slow loris, meanwhile, is protected by law in Indonesia, Singapore, Malaysia, and Thailand. Enforcing laws such as these is another important weapon in the long-term battle for conservation of the galagos, pottos, lorises, and tarsiers. ■

CAPTIVITY

Zoos the world over have long sought these curious, exotic animals for their collections, but their efforts to keep and breed them have found only mixed success over the years. The slender loris, for example, used to be quite a common exhibit, but is less often seen in zoos now because of the difficulty of keeping the animal in captivity. It has been described as a creature of "delicacy and irascible temper." Similar problems have beset attempts to keep angwantibos and needle-clawed galagos, and there are very few of any species of tarsier in captivity. Slow lorises, pottos, and greater and lesser galagos, on the other hand, are more readily exhibited and bred.

Modern advances in captive breeding—some involving hand-rearing of young—could be of conservation importance. If self-sustaining colonies of endangered species can be established in zoos, they could one day be a source for reintroducing animals to the wild in areas where they have been depleted. This is still a long way off for lorisids and tarsiers, but over the last decade the *International Zoo Yearbook* has at least recorded better success in the breeding of, among others, slender and pygmy slow lorises and Demidoff's dwarf galago. However, captive rearing and reintroduction programs can only succeed if significant progress is made in designating secure habitats in the wild—and protection of the remaining rain forests involves a race against time.

Illustration Peter Bull

INDEX

Published by Marshall Cavendish Corporation
99 White Plains Road
Tarrytown, New York 10591-9001

© Marshall Cavendish Corporation, 1997
© Marshall Cavendish Ltd, 1994

The material in this series was first published in the English language by Marshall Cavendish Limited, of 119 Wardour Street, London W1V 3TD, England.

Library of Congress Cataloging-in-Publication Data

Encyclopedia of mammals.
  p. cm.
  Includes index.
  ISBN 0-7614-0575-5 (set)   ISBN 0-7614-0580-1 (v. 5)

  Summary: Detailed articles cover the history, anatomy, feeding habits, social structure, reproduction, territory, and current status of ninety-five mammals around the world.
  1. Mammals—Encyclopedias, Juvenile. [l. Mammals—Encyclopedias.] I. Marshall Cavendish Corporation.
  QL706.2.E54 1996
  599'.003—dc20
                                                    96-17736
                                                    CIP
                                                    AC

Printed in Malaysia
Bound in U.S.A.